Soane's Favourite Subject: The Story of Dulwich Picture Gallery

Sir John Soane RA
Aged Seventy Six
Thomas Lawrence
Sir John Soane's Museum

Soane's Favourite Subject:

The Story of Dulwich Picture Gallery

Francesco Nevola

This Publication and the Exhibition 'Soane's Favourite Subject' were most generously supported by the Samuel H Kress Foundation.

Wates Residential Sales & Lettings in Dulwich Village are pleased to sponsor this inaugural exhibition at Dulwich Picture Gallery on its reopening.

Contents

Preface

Great architecture is created out of an interaction between an architect, a client and a place. This book contains much about architects and clients; it is also the history of a place. This history is of course dominated by the figure of Sir John Soane and by the Gallery he created – one of the world's seminal buildings, for all its modest scale and materials. However it is hoped that this presentation allows Soane's building (and the hundreds of other buildings he might have created at Dulwich) to be better appreciated by showing how deeply he thought about its distinguished and distinctive site.

This book is a chronological catalogue of images of Dulwich Old College and Dulwich Picture Gallery (as they are now called). We have tried to bring together every design to emerge from Soane's office. For the other architects who worked at Dulwich we have restricted ourselves to those designs which are either of considerable architectural interest or which were actually built. We have only included views of the site when they record a stage in the building history not shown elsewhere.

The purpose of this book is to make available the material needed for a understanding of Soane's design process at Dulwich and of the history of the building before and after his involvement. It offers the visual documents for a history rather than the history itself. For this reason the text concentrates more on signalling changes than on describing them in full or accounting for them. An enterprise of this kind is intended to flush out confusion and false assumptions; it is however inevitable that it will also contain some. We hope that any scholar who encounters an inaccuracy (or omission) will let us know both for our files and for any future edition.

The material in this book is very heavily indebted to the distinguished series of publications dealing with Soane's work at Dulwich produced by my predecessor, Giles Waterfield. His *Collection for a King* of 1985 offers the most comprehensive history of the Gallery and his *Soane and After* of 1987 does the same for the Gallery building. We are also greatly indebted to the architects, Murray John and Robert George, who together produced the Gallery's unpublished Conservation Plan, which contains a wealth of new material and insight. We are also most grateful to Dr. Jan Piggott, Keeper of Dulwich College Archive and author of many scholarly works on the history of the area. Dr. Piggott has provided complete access to the College archive; he has loaned most generously to this exhibition; and he has proved to be an infallible guide through the sometimes confusing history of the College and its buildings. Our warmest thanks however must go to the staff and Trustees of the Sir John Soane's Museum. Neither this exhibition nor this publication would have been possible without the most enthusiastic and wholehearted support of the Museum. They have loaned open-handedly to the exhibition; they have provided photographs at the lowest possible cost; and they have most generously waived altogether any reproduction fee. Without this vital professional partnership a publication of this kind would not be possible. The staff of the Soane Museum have also been most generous with their time and their scholarly expertise. We would like to thank in particular Susan Palmer and Stephen Astley, who have tutored all of us involved in the mysteries of Soane's archive as well as helping practically in every stage of the project. In this regard we are particularly grateful to Geremy Butler of the Soane Museum and to John Hammond for creating so many photographic images at such short notice. Francesco Nevola would also like to thank Vanessa Lacey for her support and encouragement.

This publication and the exhibition which it accompanies would never have been possible without a most generous grant from the Samuel H Kress Foundation. We are most grateful to the Foundation for helping us to provide the perfect exhibition for the re-opening of our refurbished Gallery and a publication which will (it is hoped) offer a record of the exhibition and a resource for scholars long into the future. We are also greatly indebted to Wates Residential Sales and Lettings in Dulwich Village who have proved to be the most supportive of corporate neighbours and who have shown their eagerness to help by supporting the very first of our exhibitions after re-opening.

Desmond Shawe-Taylor

Dulwich College: 1613 to 1811

Edward Alleyn (1566–1626), the founder of Alleyn's College of God's Gift, made his fortune as an actor and theatrical entrepreneur. He was the leading man of the playwright Christopher Marlowe, creating amongst others the role of Doctor Faustus. In 1594 he was recorded as an investor in the Bear Garden, and in 1600 he built the Fortune Theatre with Philip Henslowe; later, in 1604, they acquired the lucrative office of Master of Bears. Alleyn also owned three brothels on the South Bank. The earliest document connecting Edward Alleyn with Dulwich records his purchase of the Manor of Dulwich on 25 October 1605 from Sir Francis Calton for the sum of £5,000. On 17 May 1613 Alleyn is recorded as contracting the bricklayer John Benson of Westminster to build 'a chapel, a schoolhouse and twelve almshouses'. On 1 September 1616, Edward Alleyn's 50th birthday, the chapel was finally consecrated and on 21 June 1619 Alleyn obtained a patent for the incorporation of Alleyn's College of God's Gift.

The following maps and views record the appearance of the College complex when Soane first visited the site in 1811. Unfortunately no images survive to show the College buildings prior to a major remodelling undertaken in 1728–9.

We know about the uses of the College rooms from the annotated survey drawings produced by John Soane's office in 1811: the south range housed the chapel and lodgings for Warden and Master; the east range housed six old men on the ground floor with the school above and accommodation for staff and boys in the attic; the west range housed six old women on the ground floor, with the gallery above. This 'gallery' displayed the collections of Edward Alleyn himself and another actor-manager, William Cartwright (1606–86). Horace Walpole described it in 1791 as containing 'a very rich ceiling' in the process of being dismantled, and 'a hundred mouldy portraits among apostles, sibyls and kings of England'.

In addition, the survey drawings and a map of 1806 (No. 5) show several other buildings – all subsequently demolished – located to the south of the main College complex, including stables close to the present site of the Gallery, a mill and its mill pond, and two cottages. The 'Private Sittings' book of the College for 24 July 1814 records the decision to use the materials recovered from the demolished stables to build new ones and, on 16 February 1815, to demolish the mill and cottages.

2 Dulwich College *J Oliphant* 1785

3 Dulwich College *T Cadel* 1792

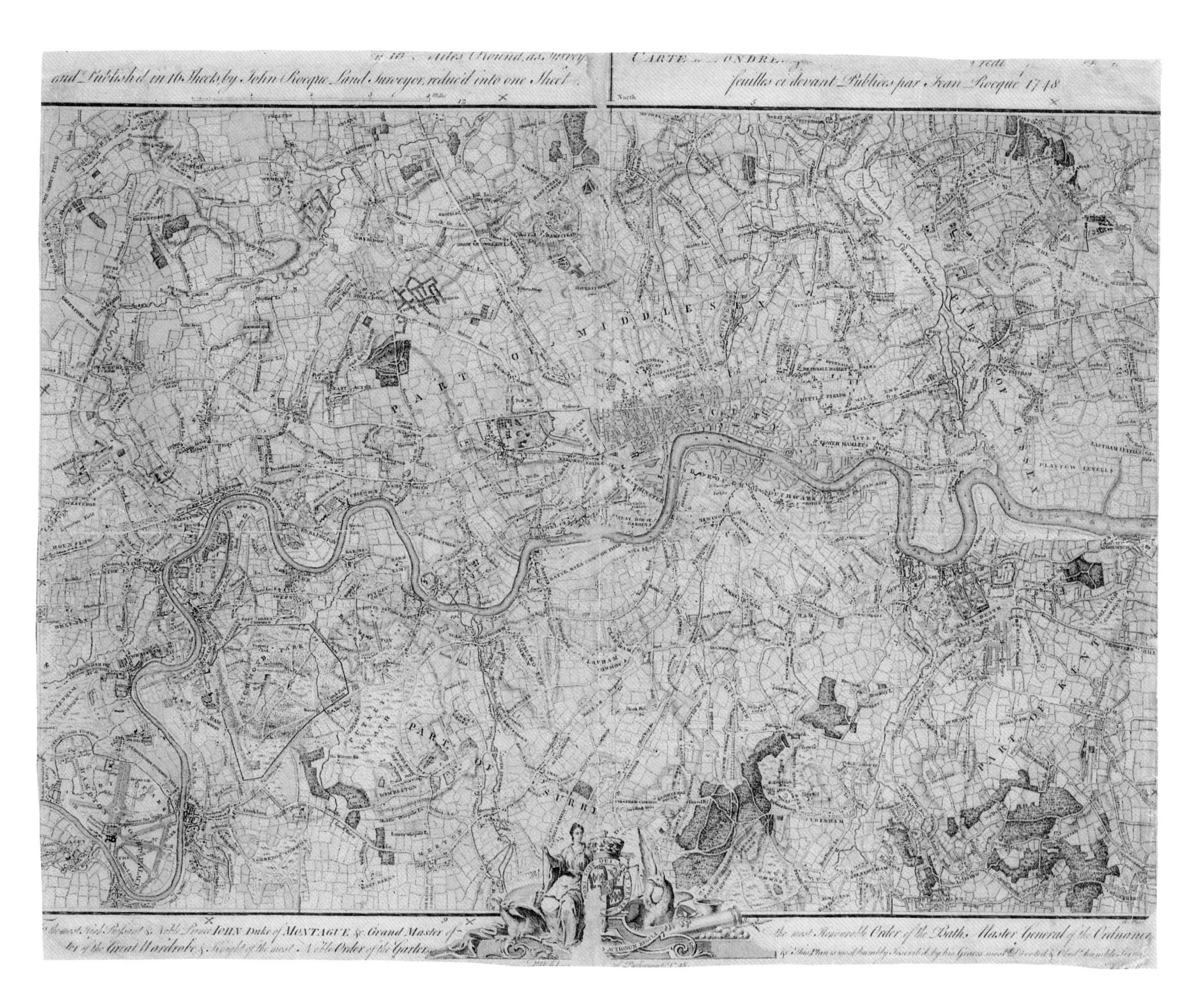

1 Map of London *Jean Rocque* 1748

4
Dulwich College
Taylor 1796

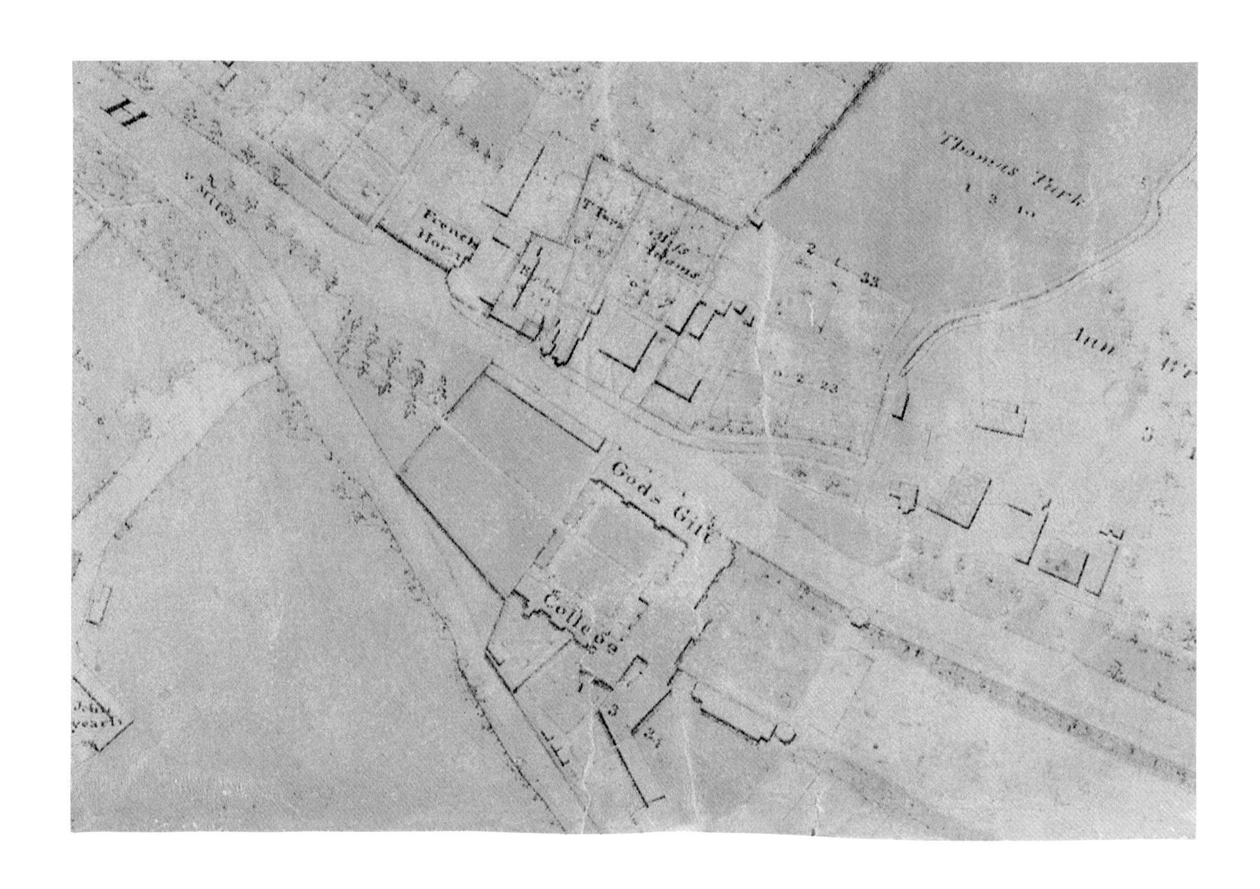

5
Map of Dulwich (Detail)
1806

The Commissioning of Sir John Soane

On 7 January 1811 Sir Peter Francis Bourgeois RA (1756–1811) died, bequeathing the precious collection of 360 paintings, that he and his friend Noel Desenfans (1744–1807) had asssembled, to Alleyn's College of God's Gift (known, by this date, as Dulwich College). Bourgeois also left £3,000 to the College of which £2,000 was to be spent on the refurbishment of the existing gallery on the top floor of the west wing of the College, with an equal sum to be raised by the College. The newly refurbished gallery was to house the Bourgeois collection along with those of Edward Alleyn and William Cartwright. Bourgeois also requested that 'some little nook of the chapel to be set apart' in order to house his body, that of his friend Noel Desenfans, and at some later date, that of Mrs Desenfans (1737–1814). For this mausoleum he had set aside £1,000 (the sum is not specified in Bourgeois's will, but it is clear from surviving accounts). In his will Bourgeois recommended Soane (who had also been his friend) as the architect for the proposed works at Dulwich College.

Bourgeois's wishes, communicated on his deathbed, are recorded in 'The Last Testament of Sir Francis Bourgeois', dated December 1810. This is a memorandum (now in Sir John Soane's Museum, Private Correspondence IX/D/2/2) written by Lancelot Baugh Allen, the College Warden until 14 April 1811, when he became Master until his retirement in 1820. Mr Corry, the Usher at Dulwich College and Bourgeois's private Chaplain was also present. Allen records that both he and Bourgeois were aware of Soane's aversion to the 'Gothic Style' – the term used at this date to describe the style of the existing Jacobean buildings of the College, and not surprisingly that preferred by the College authorities. Bourgeois got round this difficulty by referring to Inigo Jones's supposed involvement with the design of the College. Allen records Bourgeois's persuasive words: 'but your chapel is built by Inigo Jones and he [Soane] is one of his most enthusiastic admirers'.

On 8 January 1811, the day after Bourgeois's death, John Soane made his first visit to Dulwich College to inspect the site. Between February and June 1811 he sent his pupils to Dulwich to make survey drawings of the site, of which five survive (Nos. 6–10). In memory of his friend Bourgeois, Soane charged no fee for his work at Dulwich.

6

West Wing of the College: Plan and Section of the First Floor housing the Picture Gallery

G A Underwood 28 February 1811

8

West Wing of the College: East Elevation

Soane Office Early 1811?

7
West Wing of the College: East Elevation
Soane Office
Early 1811?

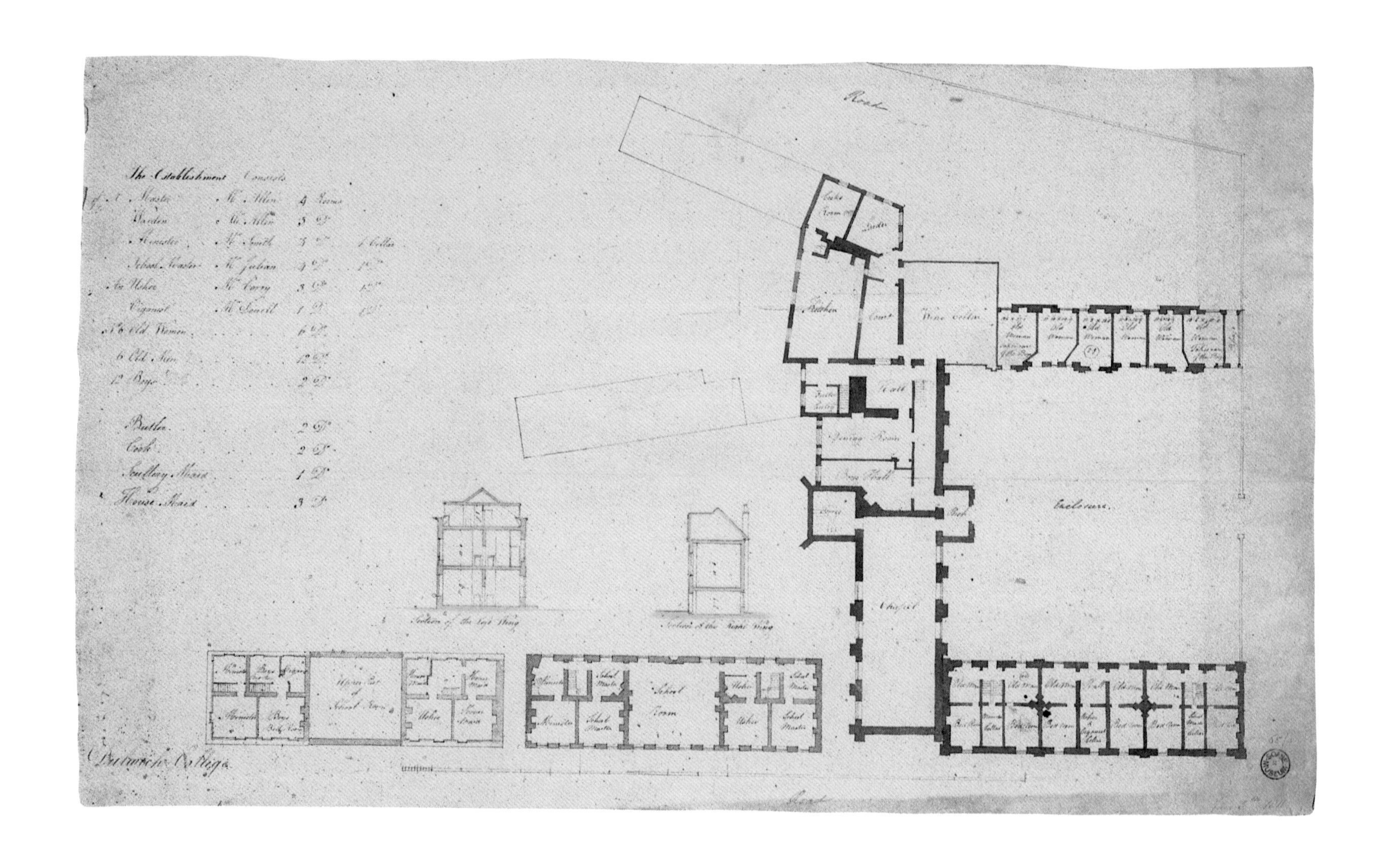

9

Ground Plan of the College, with sections of the East and West Wings

GA Underwood

5 June 1811

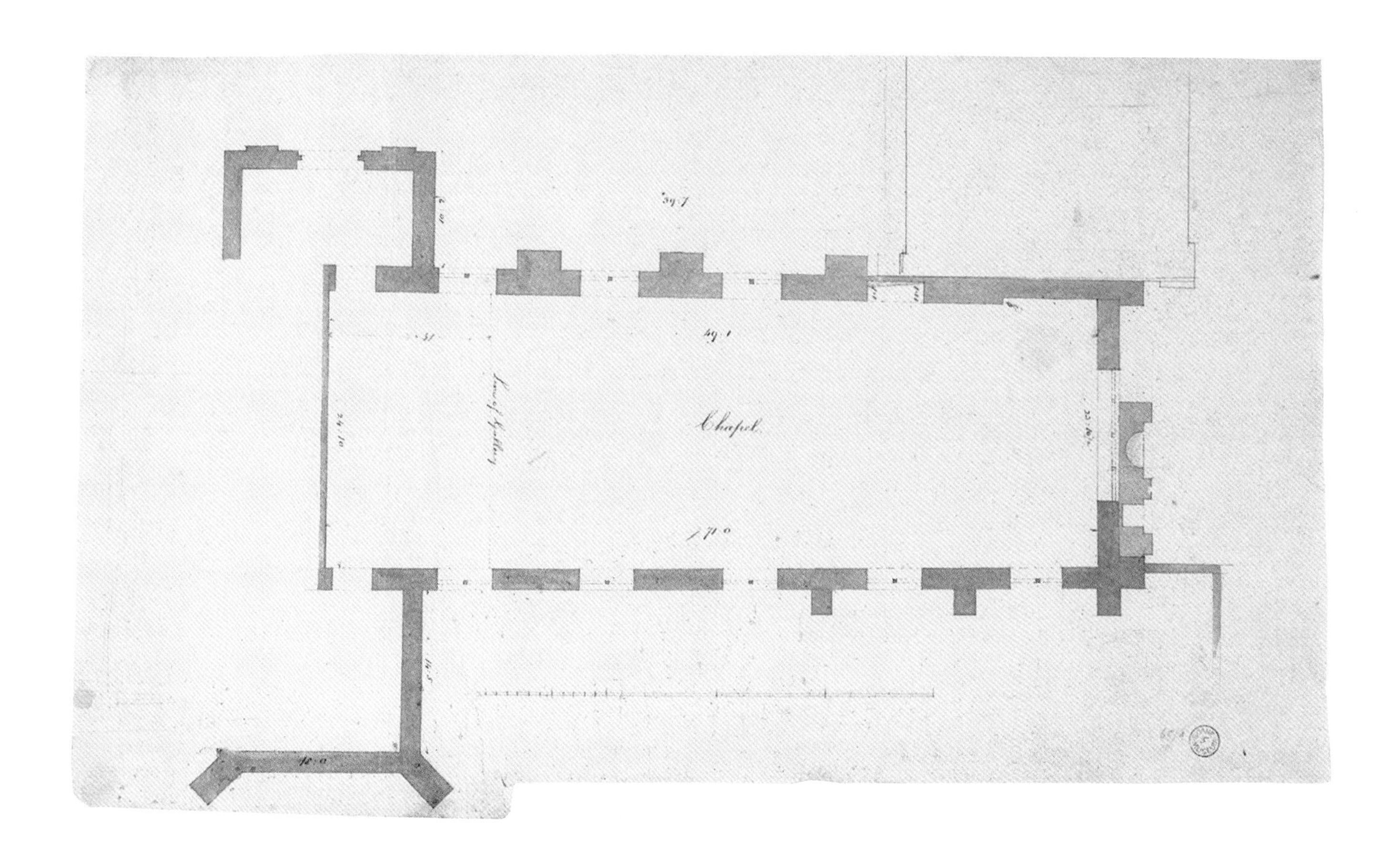

10

Plan of the Chapel

Soane Office

Early 1811?

Soane's 'Designs One to Five': April to May 1811

The following drawings are Soane's first proposals for the new building work at Dulwich, drawn during the months of April and May 1811. They are typical of Soane's working method in offering a number of possible designs, from which the client could choose. A note in Soane's diary records his submission of these five designs to the College on Thursday 16 May 1811: 'Left 5 different Designs, L[ay]out: Drawings & Settled Gen[eral] Est[imate]: Estimate of Gallery & Finished & Mausol [eum]: ab[out] £8,000 on a rough Calcul[ation].' These drawings are evidently not for the refurbishment of the gallery in the west wing of the College, as envisaged in Bourgeois's will. Instead Soane proposed erecting an almost completely new college quadrangle to the south of the old one, demolishing the original east and west wings and radically remodelling the south wing.

Unlike most architects at this date, Soane provided clients with perspective views in watercolour, as well as plans and elevations, to show how a building might actually look in natural daylight and in its surrounding landscape. This picturesque approach was similar to that adopted by Humphrey Repton to show off his garden designs to potential clients. To this end Soane invested much time and money training his pupils in the artifice of perspective.

Soane's first five designs for the new Gallery at Dulwich College are presented in a series of finished plan and perspective views. These drawings show the architect's different ideas overlapping and evolving – sometimes a drawing which appears to represent one design may include variants pointing forward to the next. The first three drawings of this series, numbered 1 to 3 in the top left corner (Nos. 15, 16 and 17), all represent what Soane calls 'Design No. 1', but they do not correspond in details as significant as the location of the Gallery and mausoleum. Instead they explore various design options.

By the late 1780s, having established his office (which included between four and six pupils, a paid assistant a surveyor and several clerks of works), Soane rarely produced finished drawings himself. Instead, he made vigorous but imprecise sketches, leaving a pupil to turn them into neat, scaled drawings. These finished sheets were then often drawn over in pencil, probably by Soane, to solve some new design problem, which again the pupil was left to work up.

Several of these finished drawings are dated which allows specific pupils to be identified as the draughtsman. Soane's 'Day-Books' record the activities of every one of his pupils; they even tell us what time they arrived for work in the morning. George Basevi (1794–1845), the future architect of the Fitzwilliam Museum in Cambridge, consistently arrived five minutes early; Robert Chantrell, Soane's pupil from 1807 to 1814 and later the Surveyor of York Minster, on the other hand regularly arrived fifteen to twenty minutes late.

Note: In all but very rare cases Soane orientates his plans and views with north to the right – as if viewed from College Road. Existing buildings to be retained are marked in grey; new building in red.

11

Design for the New Gallery: Front and Rear Elevation

Soane Office April 1811?

12

Design for the Entrance Façade of the Gallery

GA Underwood 4 April 1811

13
Design for the Entrance Façade of the Gallery
Soane Office April 1811?

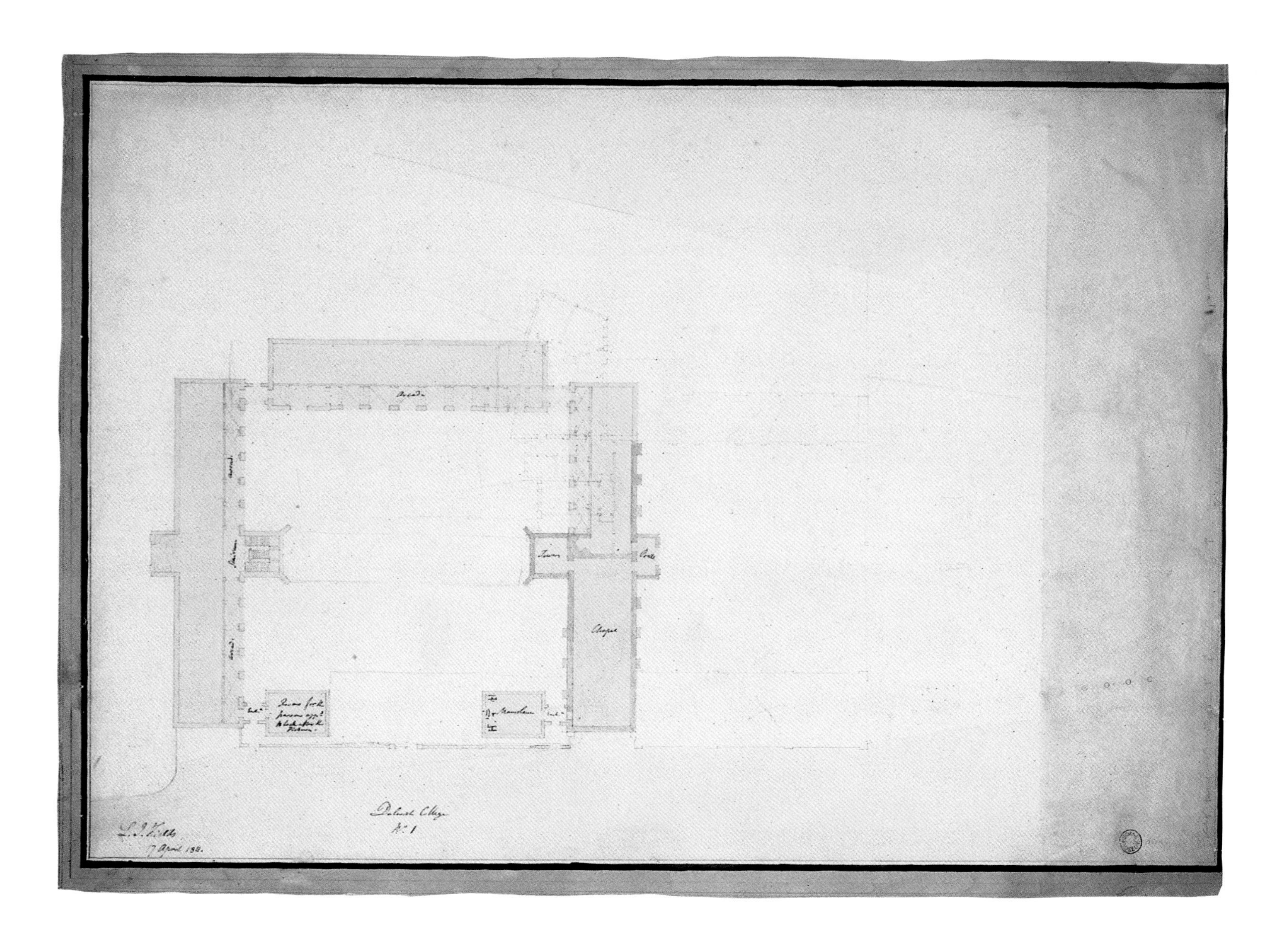

14 Dulwich College and Gallery: Design No. 1. Plan for a Quadrangle *G Bailey* 17 April 1811

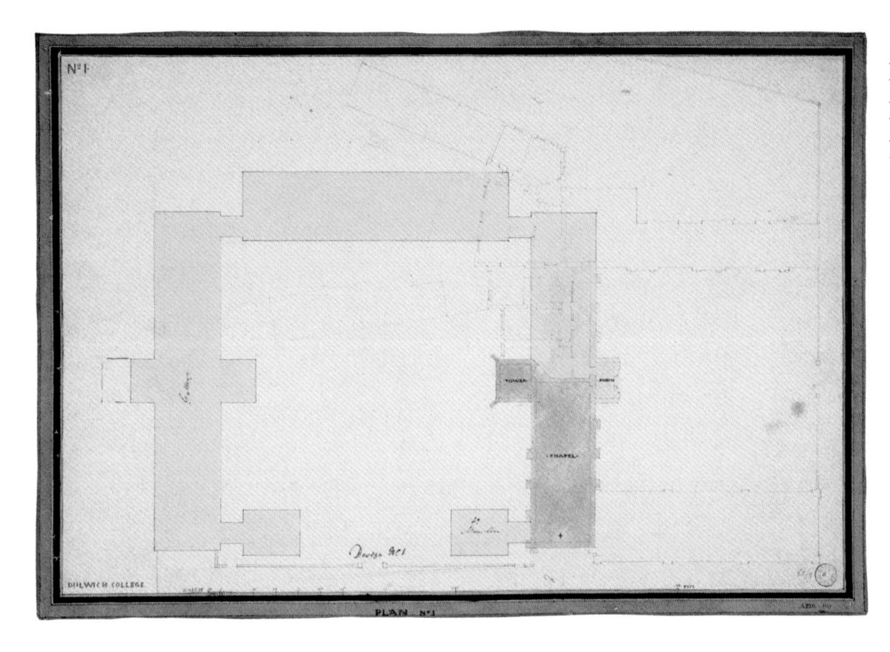

15

Dulwich College and Gallery: Design No. 1, Drawing No. 1. Plan

Soane Office April 1811

17

Dulwich College and Gallery: Design No. 1, Drawing No. 3. Perspective View

Soane Office May 1811

16

Dulwich College and Gallery: Design No. 1, Drawing No. 2. Perspective View

G Bailey 17 April 1811

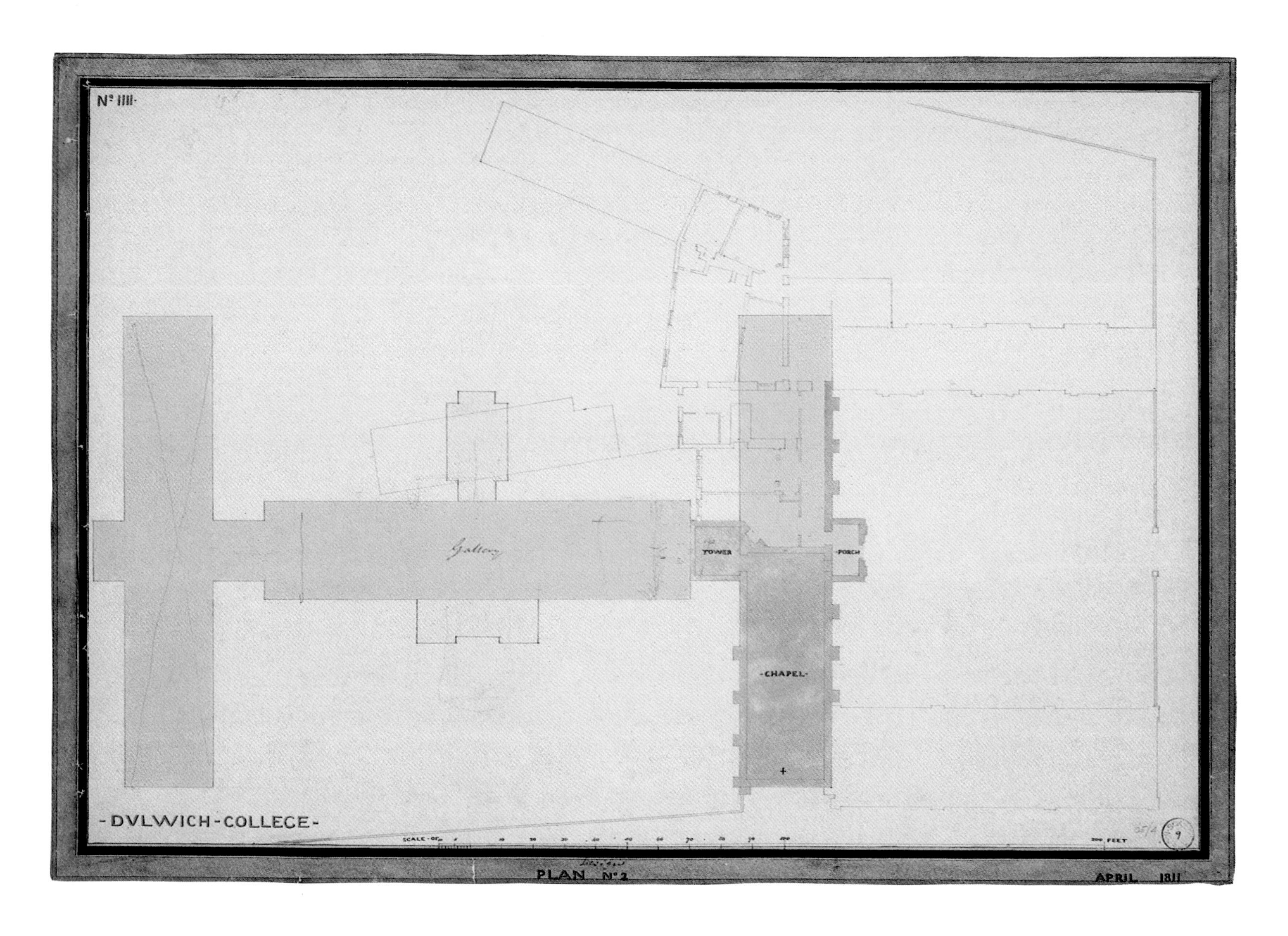

18

Dulwich College and Gallery: Design No. 2, Drawing No. 4. Plan

Soane Office April 1811

19

Dulwich College and Gallery: Design No. 2. Drawing No. 5. Perspective View

G Bailey 17 April 1811

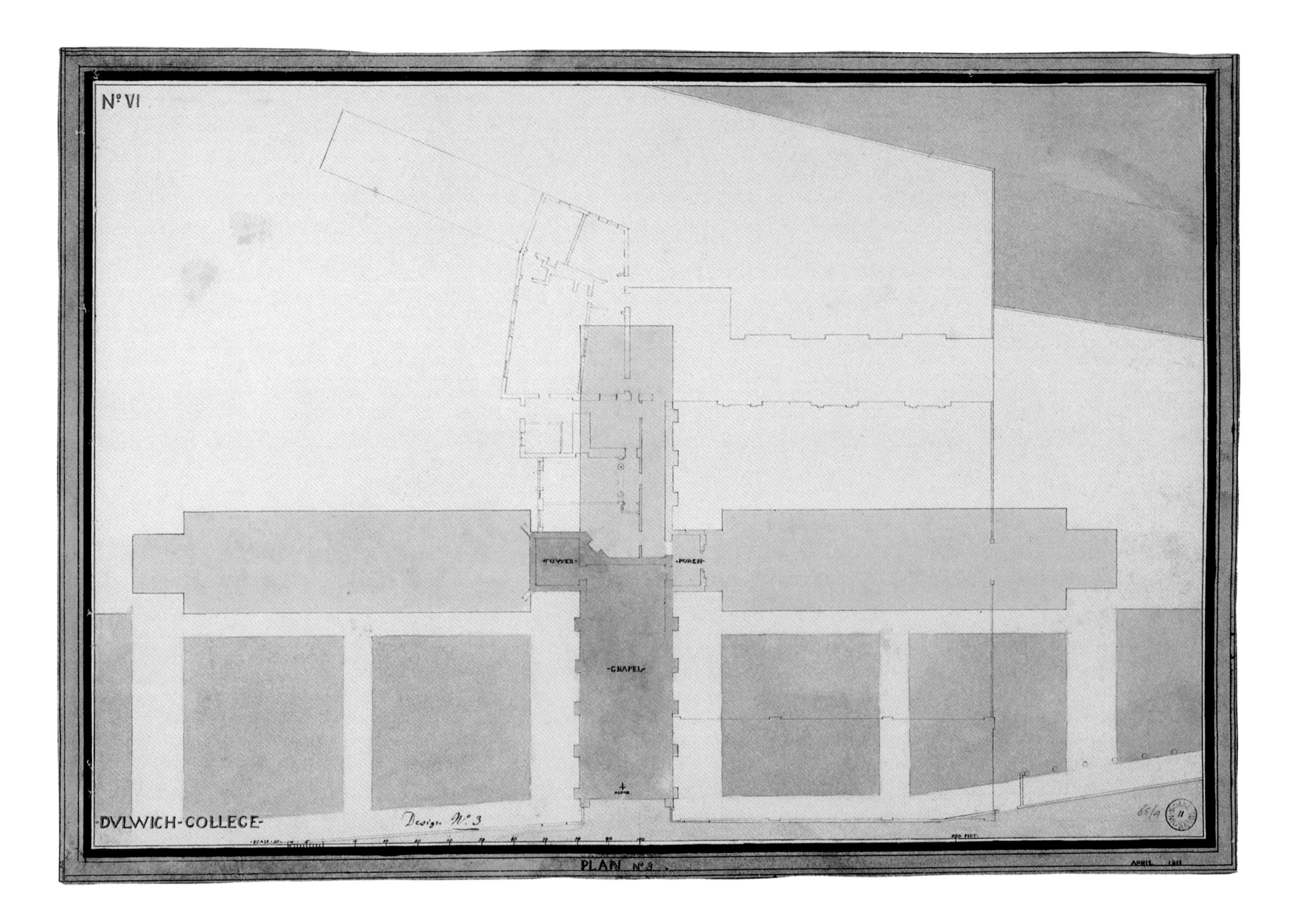

20

Dulwich College and Gallery: Design No. 3, Drawing No. 6. Plan

Soane Office April 1811

21

Dulwich College and Gallery: Design No. 3, Drawing No. 7. Perspective View

Soane Office April 1811?

22

Design for the Entrance Façade of the Gallery

G Bailey or *GA Underwood* 29 April 1811

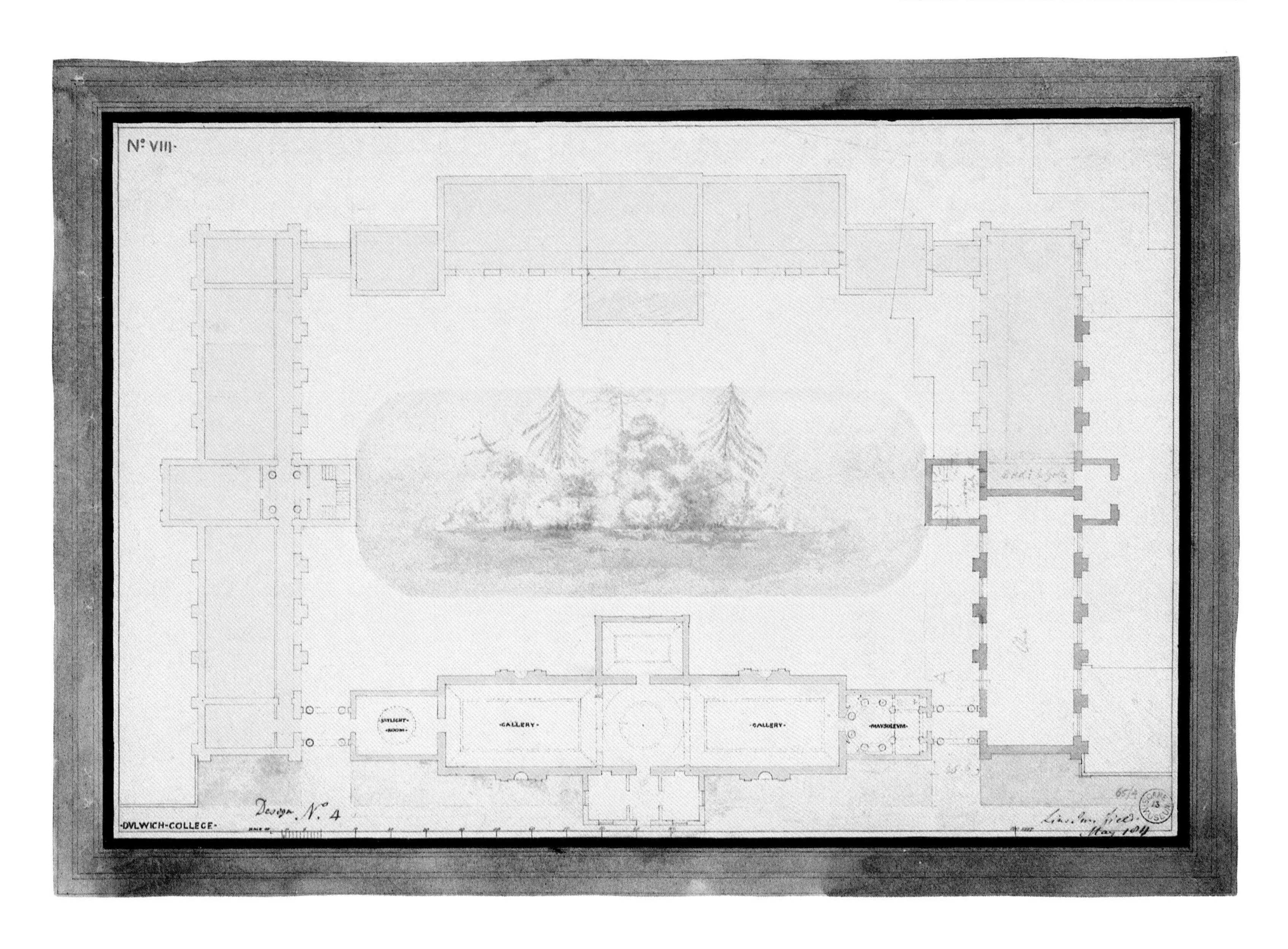

23

Dulwich College and Gallery: Design No. 4, Drawing No. 8. Plan

Soane Office May 1811

24

Dulwich College and Gallery: Design Nos. 4 and 5, Drawing No. 10. Perspective View

Soane Office May 1811

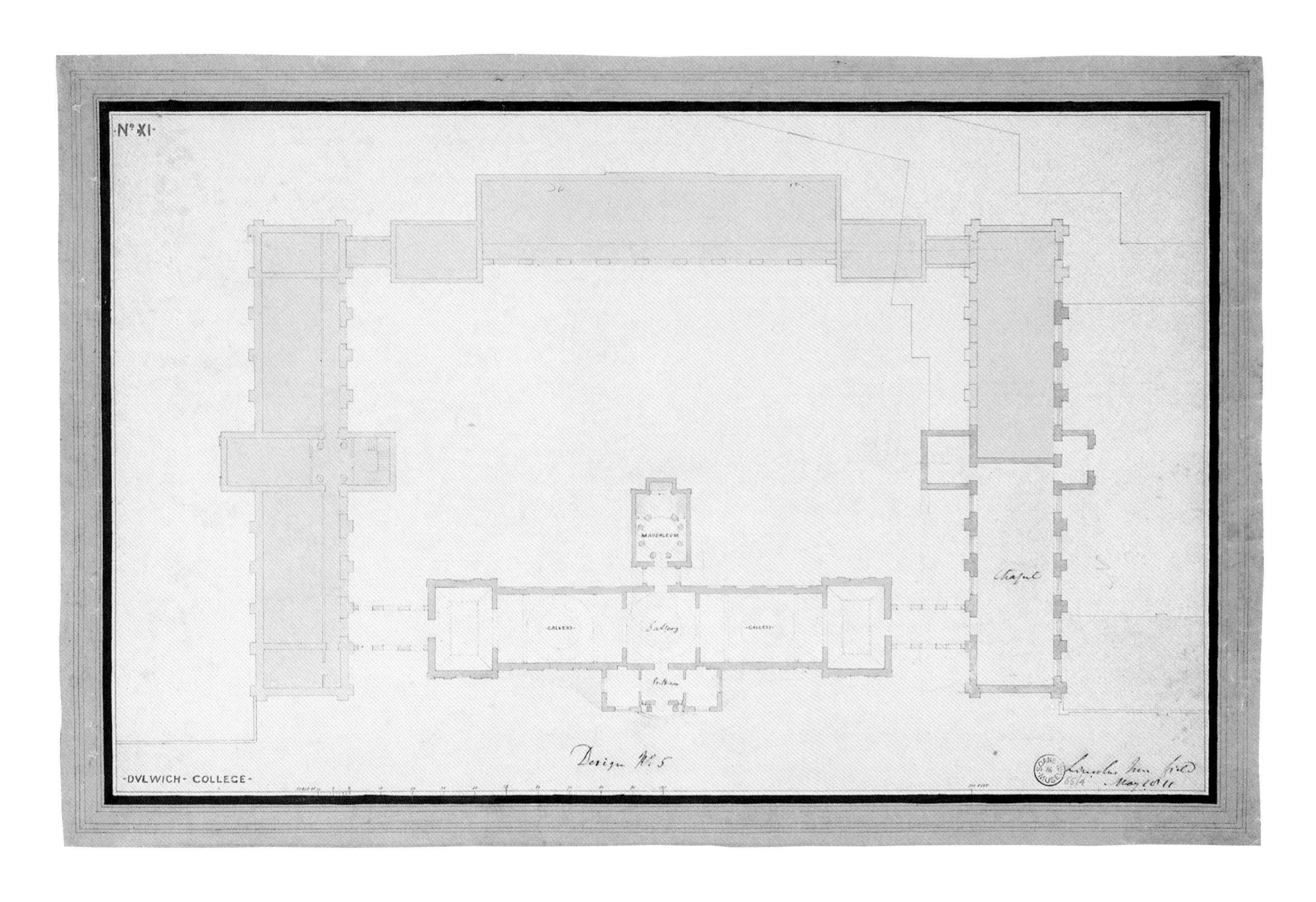

25
Dulwich College and Gallery: Design No. 5, Drawing No. 11. Plan
Soane Office May 1811

26

The Interior of the Gallery: Design No. 5, Drawing No. 12. Perspective View

Soane Office May 1811

27

The Interior of the Gallery. Perspective View

Soane Office May 1811?

28

Section through the Gallery with a Single Storey Mausoleum

Soane Office May 1811?

29
Interior Perspective of the Mausoleum
JM Gandy? 1811

Soane's 'Designs Six to Eight': May 1811

Following the rejection by the College authorities on 16 May 1811 of all five designs for the new buildings, Soane made a note in his diary for Sunday 19 May: 'Mr Corri, J. Wariter [?], Warden called – mark plan on site of kitch[en]: & old women under'. The Warden seems to have instructed Soane to pursue the idea of a single new wing combining the Picture Gallery and old women's almshouses on the site of the old kitchen – which occupied the south west corner of the College (see No. 9). The following group of drawings offer three distinct proposals (which Soane calls 'Design Nos. 6, 7 and 8') for this new wing. In his diary, Soane records a visit to Mr Allen on Friday 24 May, presumably to discuss the architect's latest ideas. On Saturday 25 May, perhaps as a result of this visit, Soane produced his 'Design No. 7' (No. 32), which is remarkably close to the Gallery as built.

Some things have not changed: the Gallery interiors (when shown) are still as they appear in Nos. 26–29 and Soane continued to dream of a new quadrangle, including the outline of a south wing in all these plans.

30

Dulwich College and Gallery: Design No. 6. Plan

Soane Office May 1811?

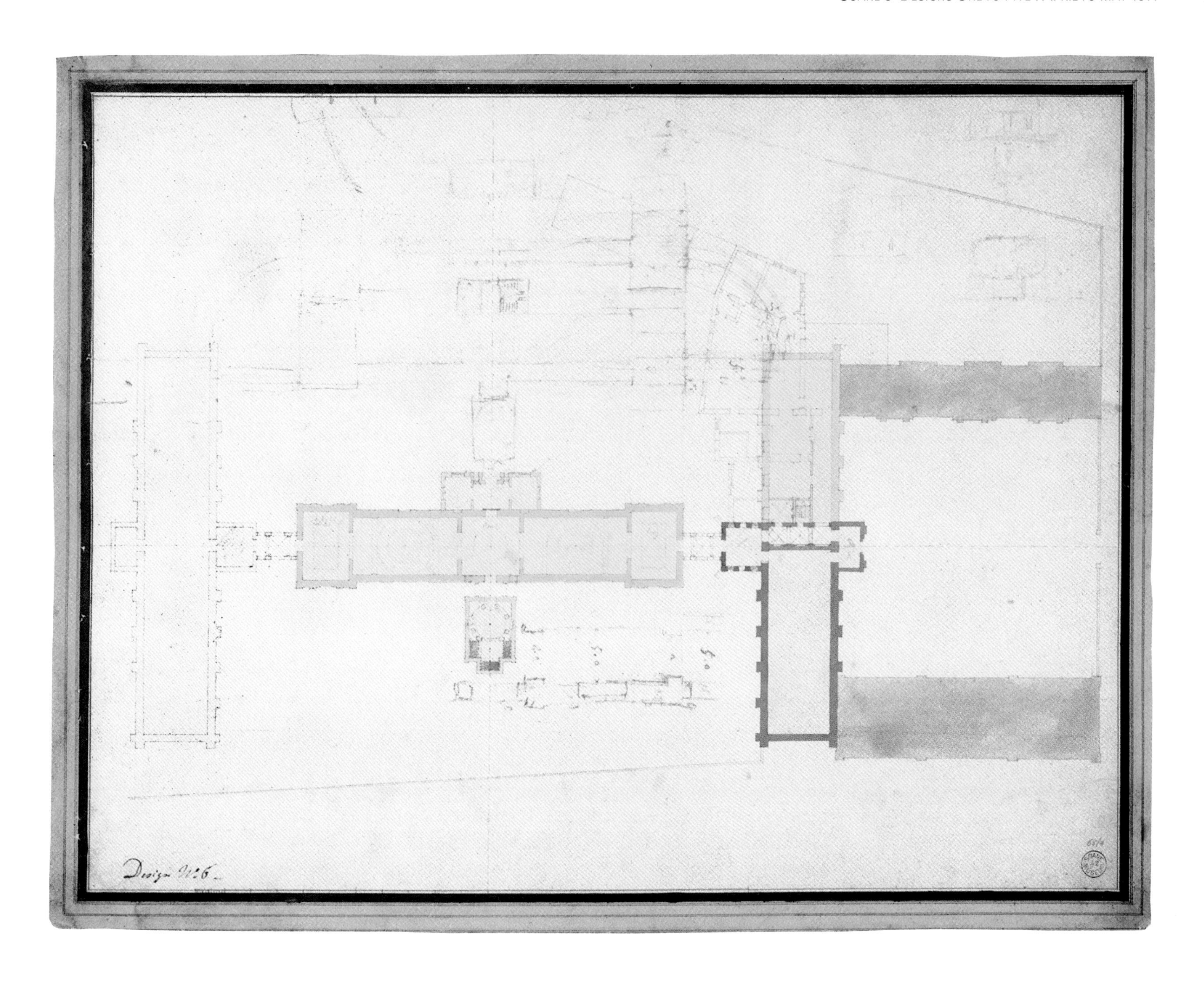
Design No. 6

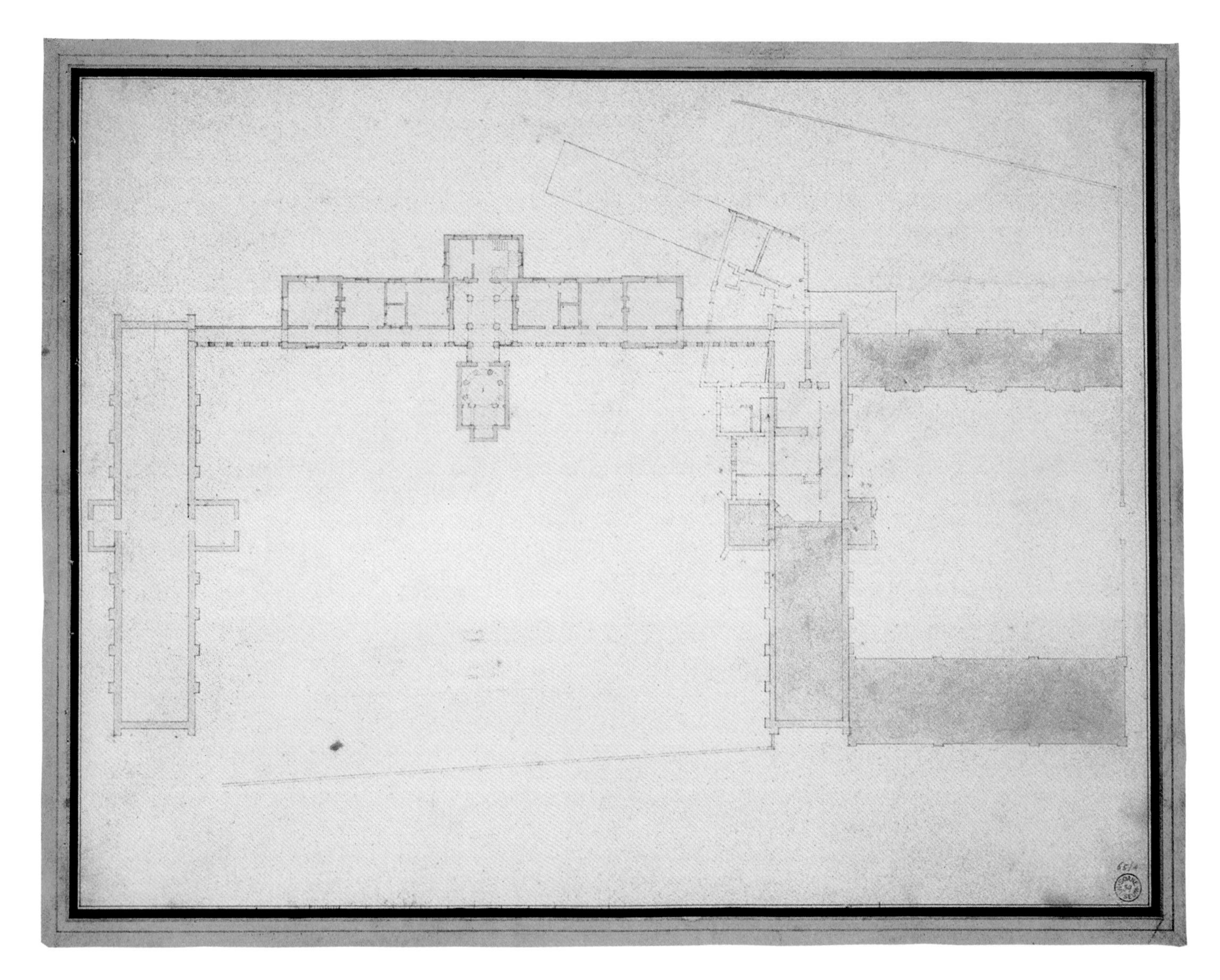

31

Dulwich College: Ground Floor Plan of Two-Storey Gallery Block showing Almshouses and Mausoleum (Gallery above)

Soane Office May 1811?

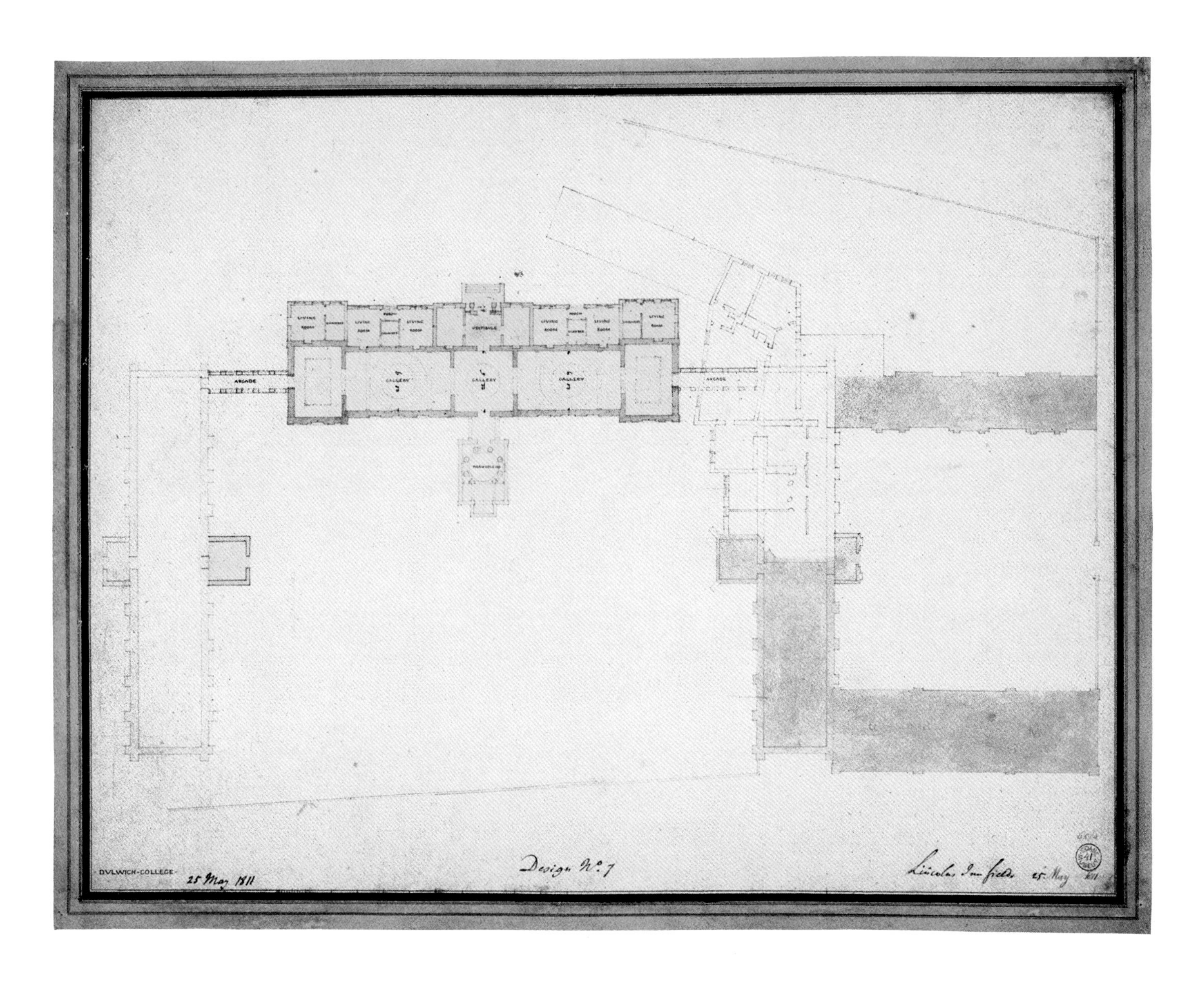

32
Dulwich College and Gallery: Design No. 7. Plan of the Gallery Block
J Buxton 25 May 1811

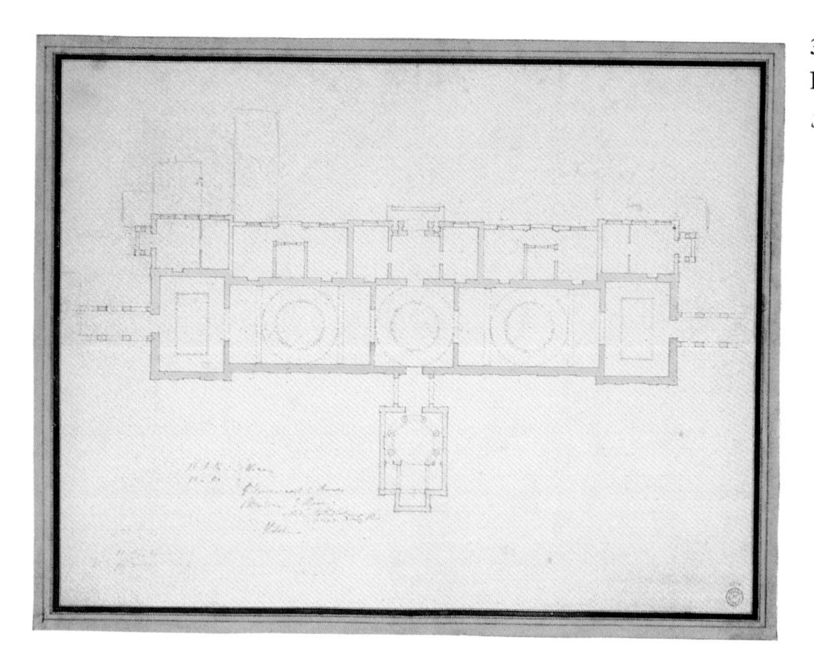

33

Plan of the Gallery

Soane Office May 1811?

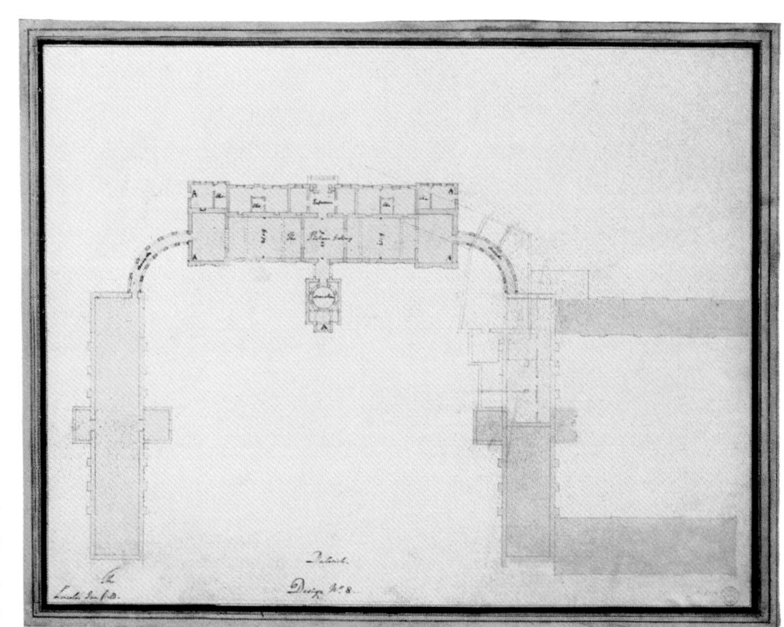

34

Dulwich College and Gallery: Design No. 8. Plan

Soane Office May 1811?

35
West Elevation of the Gallery Block
Soane Office May 1811

The Approved Design: 12 July 1811

After his conversation with Mr Allen on 24 May, Soane's next recorded meeting with the College authorities did not take place until 12 July 1811. This event is documented in Soane's diary and in the 'Private Sittings' books of the College. Two of Soane's plans also bear the names of all those present at the meeting. The Sittings books record Soane's opinion that 'from the ruinous state of the present West Wing ... the whole must be taken down', and that 'to build in our back yard at right angles to our present Kitchen would be a more convenient scite [sic] to erect such Picture Gallery'. The College never did agree to demolish their west wing (which has yet to fall down), but they must have realised it was not large enough to house Bourgeois's collection (as Bourgeois had imagined). Instead they gave their approval to the idea, the siting and the design of Soane's entirely new block, with its unusual combination of Picture Gallery, mausoleum and almshouses, resolving 'that it is expedient if possible to carry such plan into execution immediately'.

Soane estimated the cost of the new building at £11,800 (though not recorded in the minutes this figure can be deduced from the accounts in the 'Private Sittings' book). The College had £5,800 in their rebuilding fund; Mrs Desenfans was ready to cede Sir Francis Bourgeois's legacy of £2,000 on the condition that the Gallery should be erected immediately, and the executors of Bourgeois's will would provide £1,000 for the mausoleum. For building work to go ahead a further £3,000 needed to be raised. Soane 'offered to assist the College in making up any deficiency', but his offer was firmly yet gratefully refused. Before committing to 'business of such serious importance', the College wished to 'take due precaution that the estimate be not exceeded and that the work be done according to the estimate; so that we may be justified by having some assurance in writing'. For this reason the building work was stalled while Soane had to invite workmen to tender for the works, a practice he evidently disliked.

Soane came to the meeting on 12 July with what is essentially a single consistent design, presented on five separate sheets, which he had worked up from his 'Design No. 7' of the previous group. Being Soane, however, these designs include some choices. Some pencil additions probably added during the meeting mostly concern the option of an arcade running across the east façade of the new building, which the College finally approved.

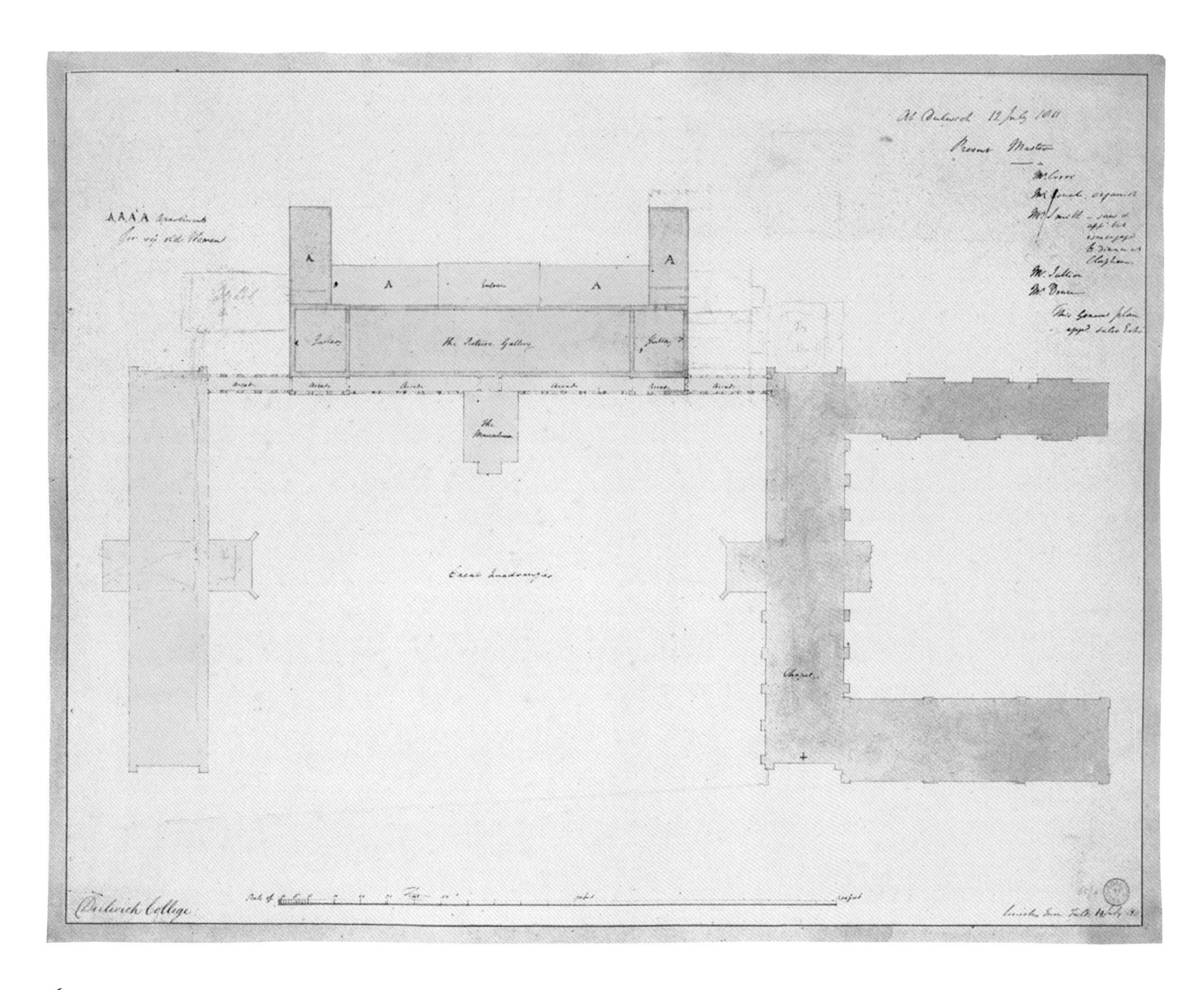

36

Plan of the Gallery and College Buildings

G Bailey or *J Buxton* 10 July 1811

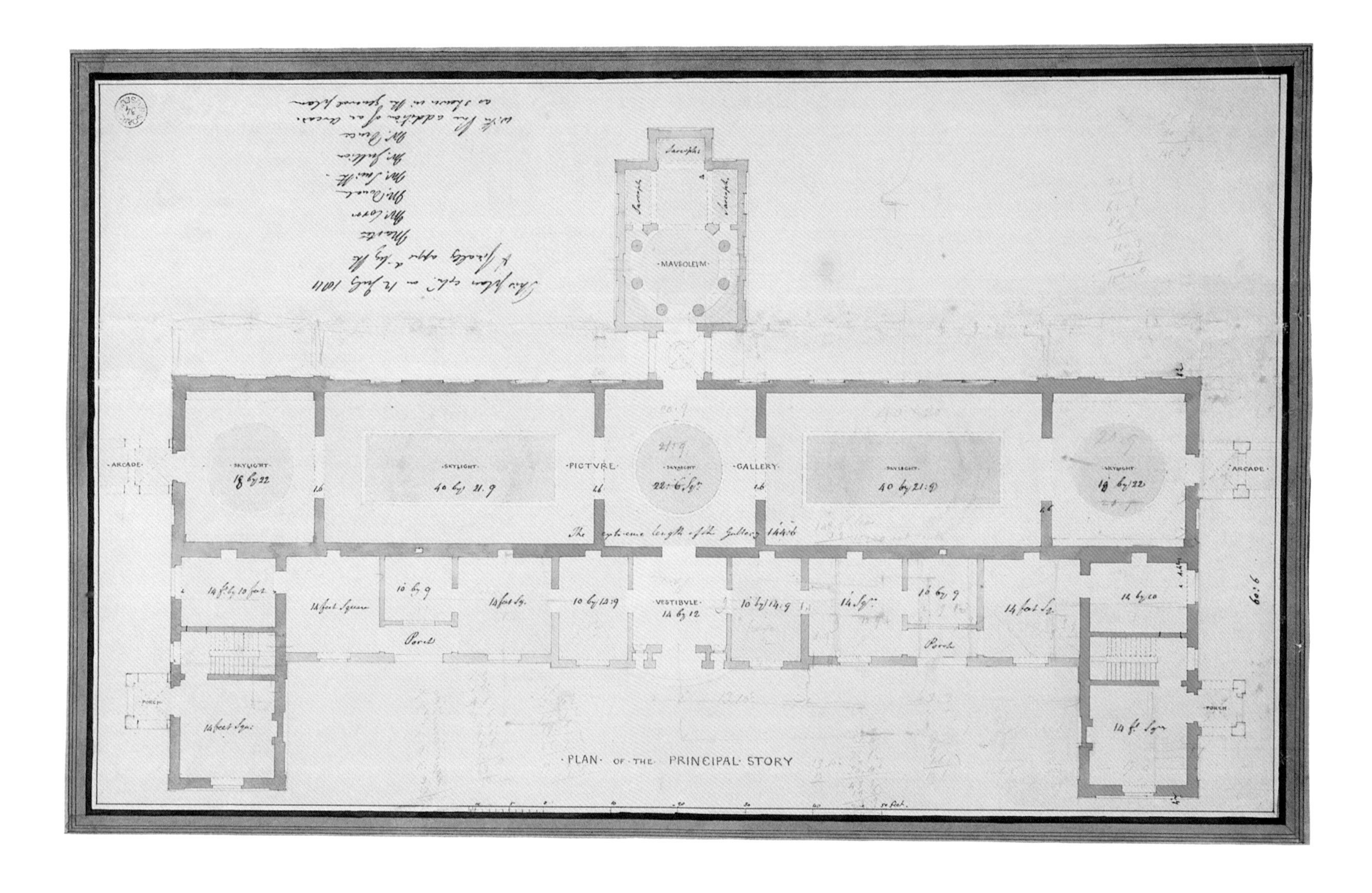

37

Plan of the Gallery

G Bailey or *J Buxton* 10 July 1811

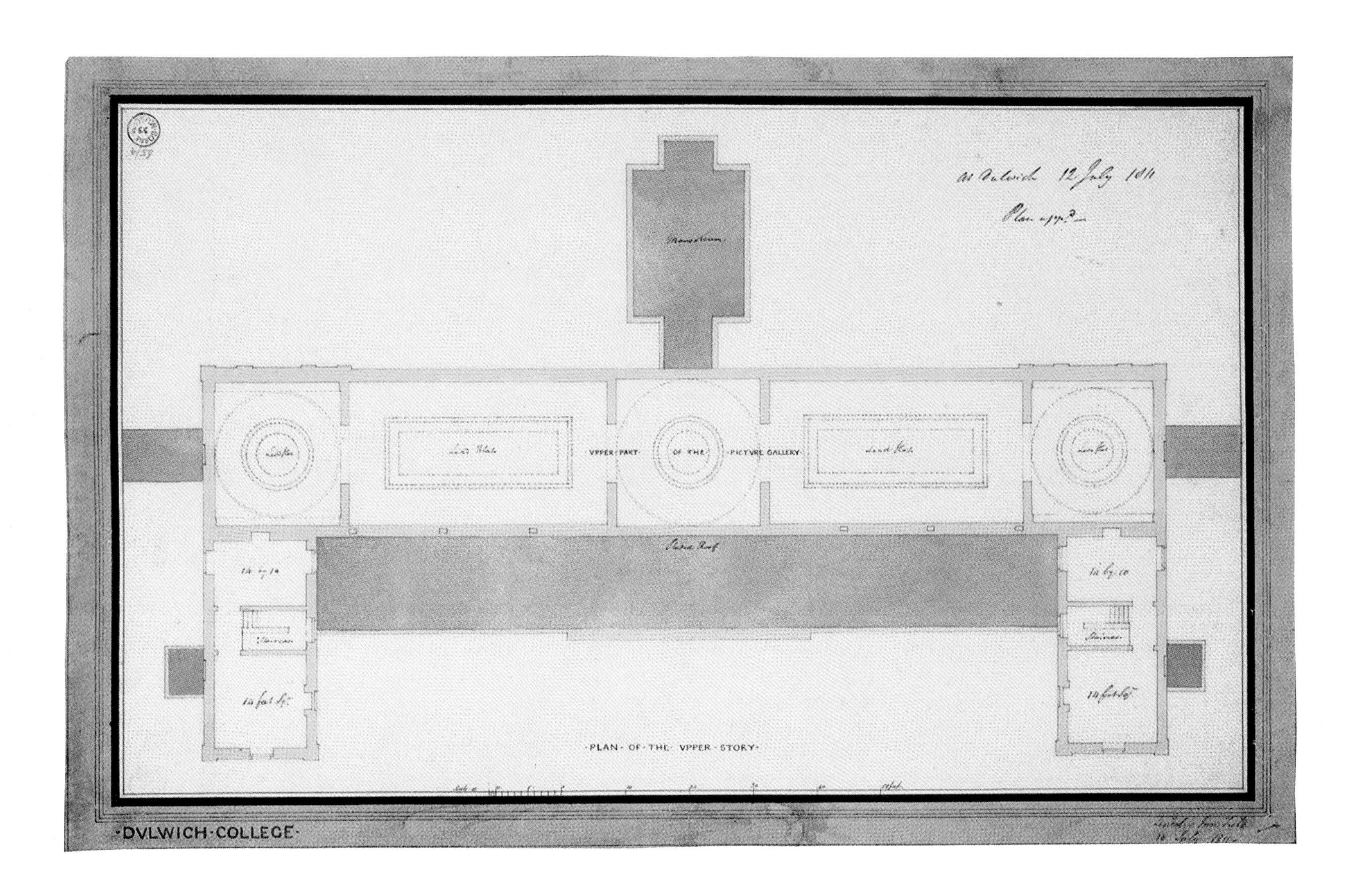

38
Plan of the Upper Storey of the Gallery
G Bailey or *J Buxton* 10 July 1811

39

West Elevation of the Gallery

G Bailey 10 July 1811

40
East Elevation of the Gallery
G Bailey 10 July 1811

From Approved Design to Foundation Stone: 12 July to 19 October 1811

Throughout July and August, Soane's office developed the plans he had presented on 12 July. Even at this stage Soane continued to produce new drawings with significant alterations. On 17 July he moved the mausoleum (a single-storey structure) to the west façade to create an austere, unbroken arcade on the east façade. On 21 July, a few days later, the mausoleum was back on the east façade and now on a much grander scale. In the following weeks Soane and his office worked on improving this latter design. An interesting aspect of this group of drawings is the elimination of all but the occasional trace of the Jacobean elements seen in the designs so far.

In a letter of 5 August 1811 Soane informed the College authorities that he had managed to reduce his estimate from £11, 800 to £11,270, by building 'in a plain and substantial manner'. Soane had also put the project out to tender, though he himself preferred to work with his own team of loyal builders. He found 'no reason to alter my opinion of the expense of executing the designs proposed', but committed 'to economise the expenditure as far as is consistent with solidity and durability of construction'. The College responded on 22 August 1811 by asking for a written contract with the builders tying them to their estimates. Even with these assurances the Governors were still short of £2, 500 and hesitating before committing to the project.

It was Margaret Desenfans who broke the dead-lock. On 19 September 1811 she wrote to Soane offering money for the completion of the building, adding that 'the only consolation [she] can receive in this life will be to see the wishes and intentions of her dear friend Sir Francis Bourgeois, carried into effect in the most compleat and expeditious manner'. This offer of £4,000 was made to the College authorities on 26 September 1811; the foundations of the new building were laid on 19 October 1811.

42

East Elevation of the Gallery (half)

Soane Office July 1811?

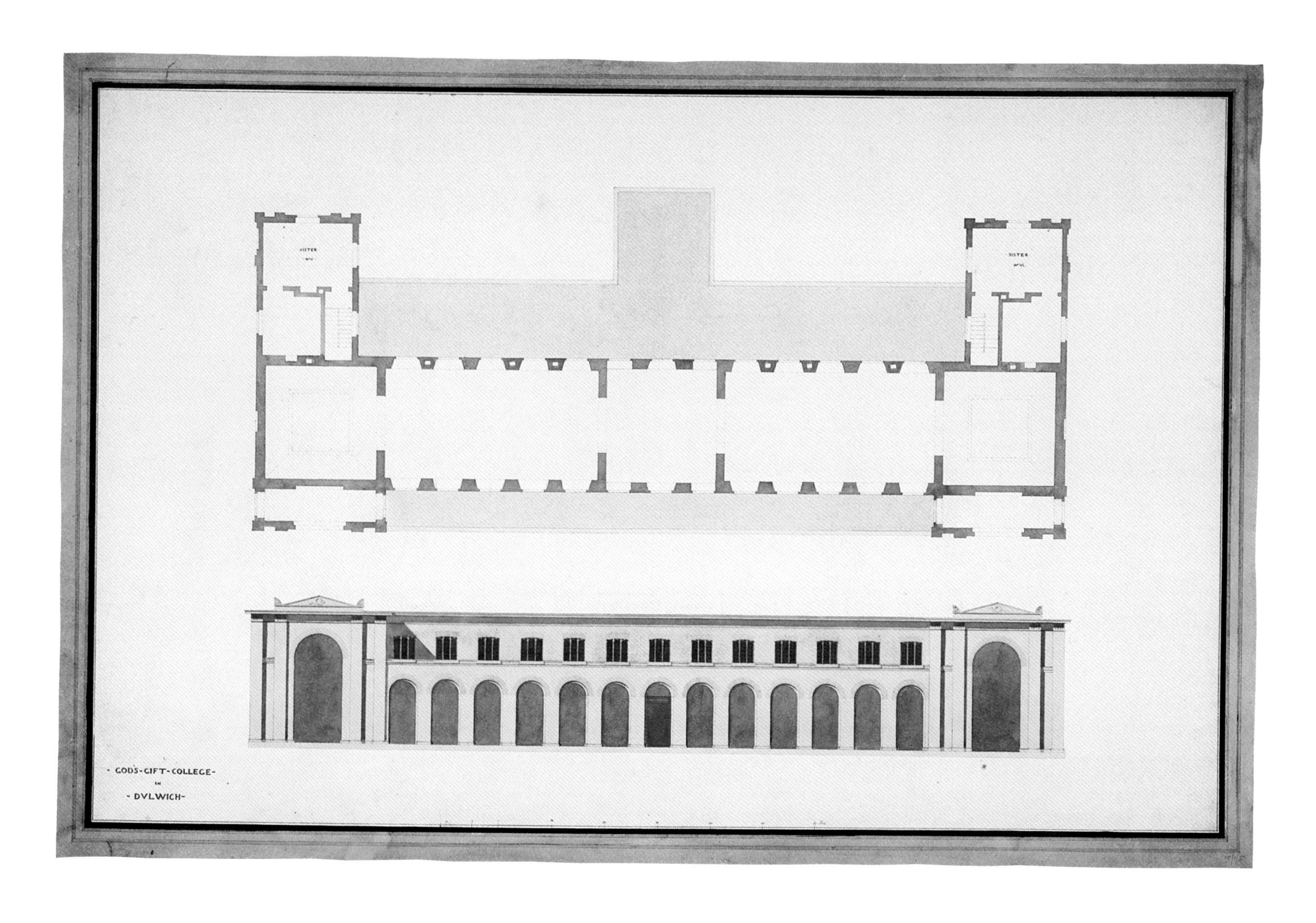

41

East Elevation and Second-Storey Plan of the Gallery

G Bailey, GA Underwood, or *G Basevi* 17 July 1811

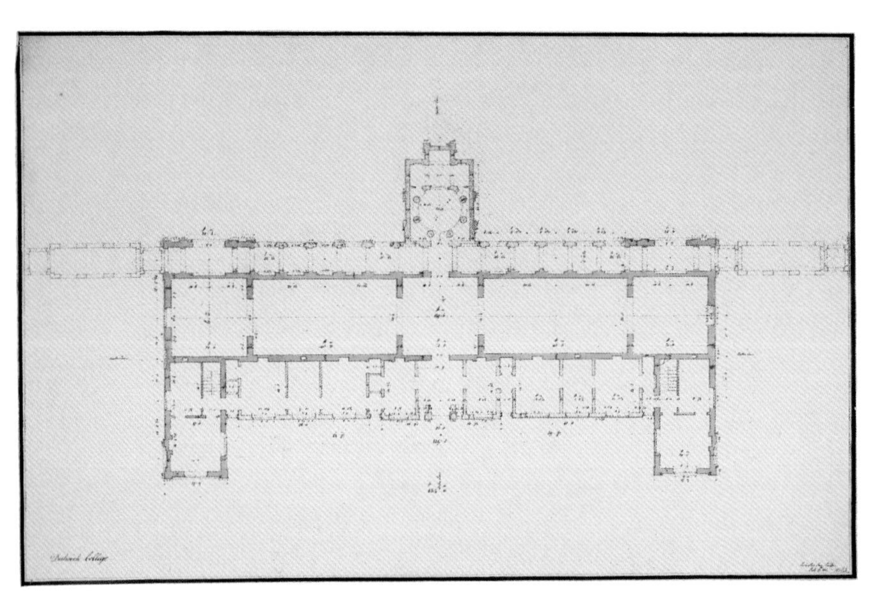

43
Plan of the Gallery
G Bailey, GA Underwood, or G Basevi 17 July 1811

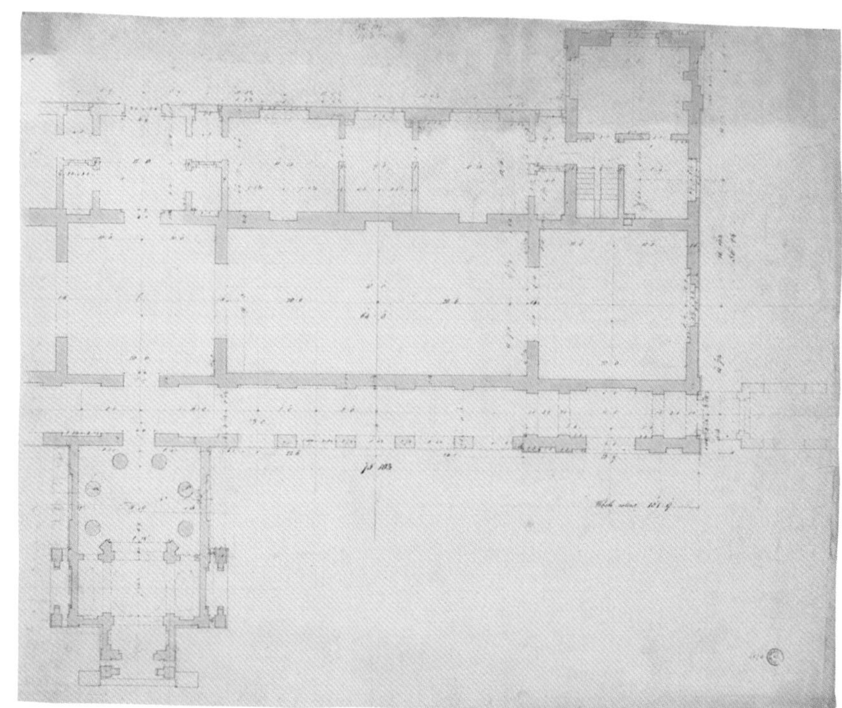

45
Half Plan of the Gallery
Soane Office July 1811?

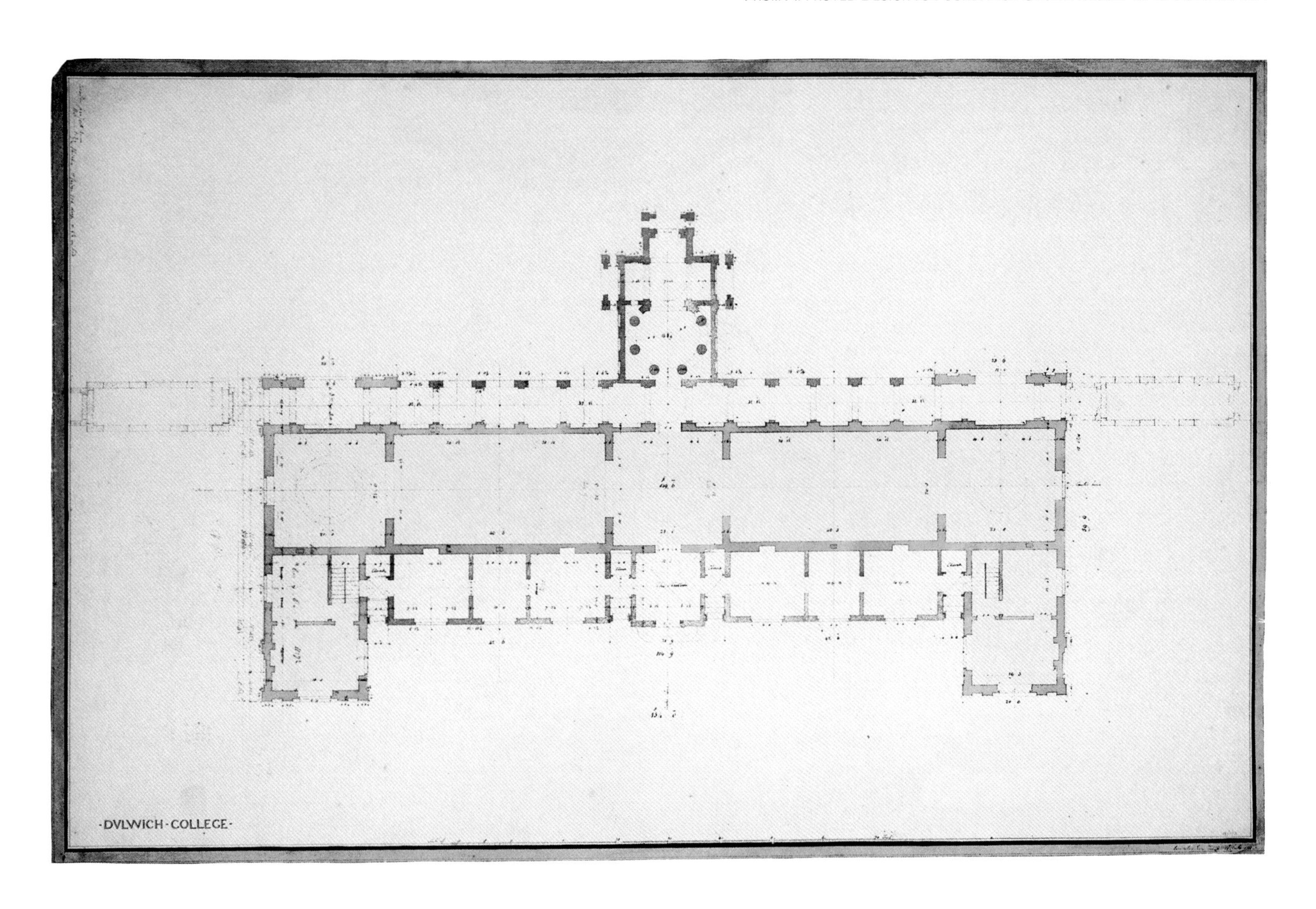

44
Plan of the Gallery
G Bailey, GA Underwood, G Basevi, or *J Buxton* 19 July 1811

46

Perspective View of the East Façade with Mausoleum

John Soane 21 July 1811

47
Perspective View of the East Façade with Mausoleum
G Bailey, GA Underwood, J Buxton or *G Basevi* 22 July 1811

48
Perspective View of the East Façade with Mausoleum
Soane Office July 1811?

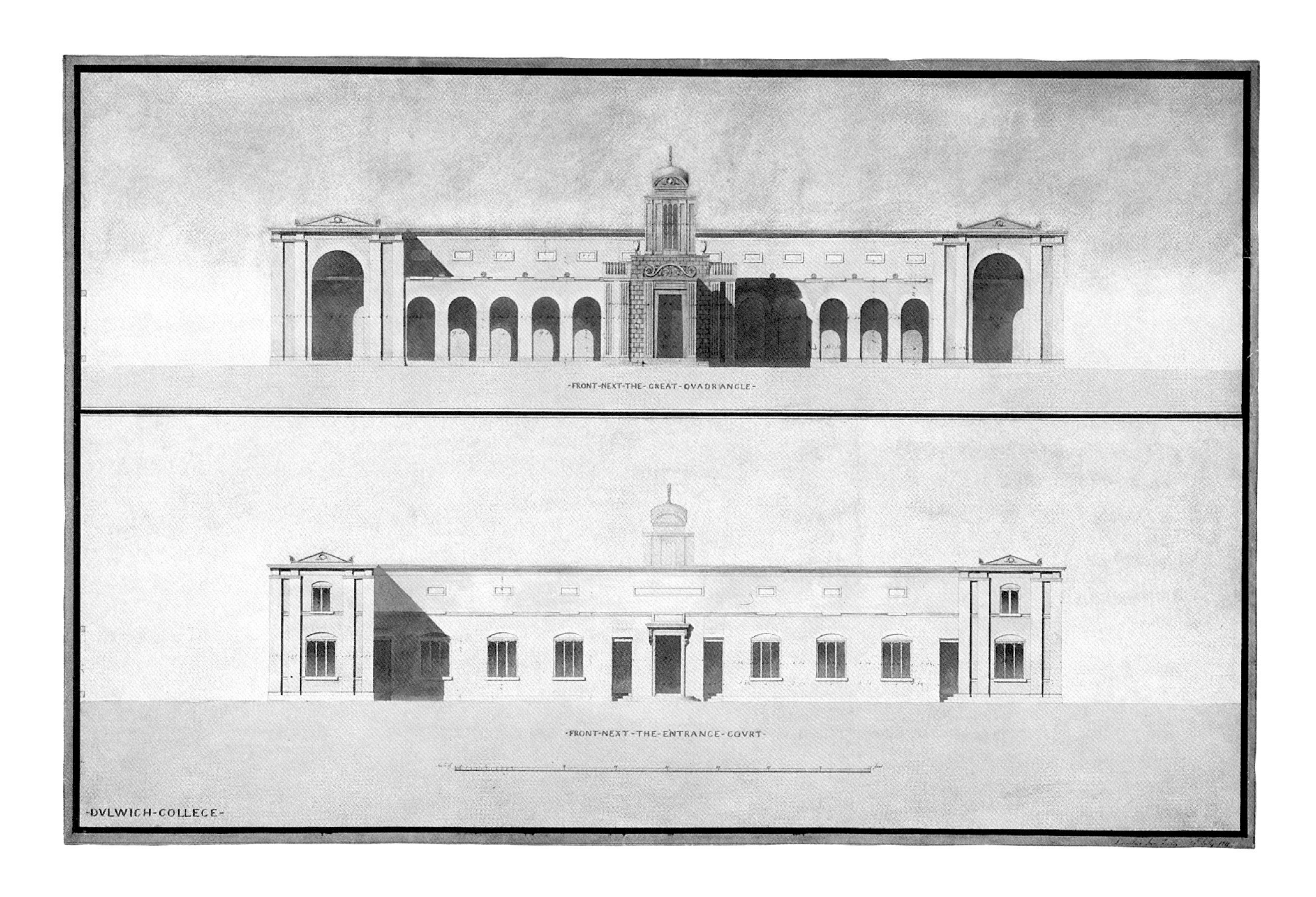

49
East and West Elevations of the Gallery
GA Underwood 29 July 1811

50

West Elevation of the Gallery

Soane Office August 1811?

51

East-West Section through the Gallery and Mausoleum

Soane Office July or August 1811?

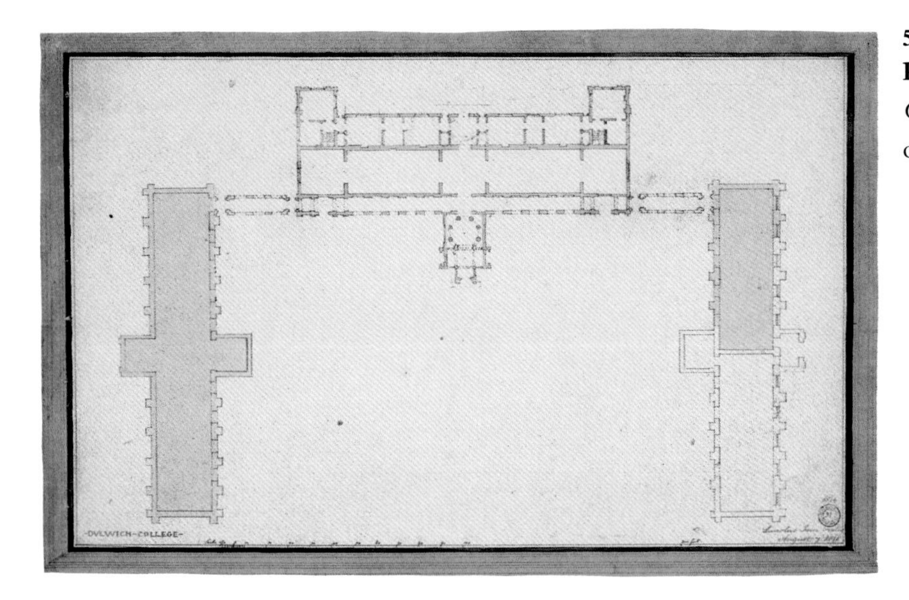

52

Plan of the Gallery and College Buildings

G Bailey; GA Underwood
or *G Basevi* 7 August 1811

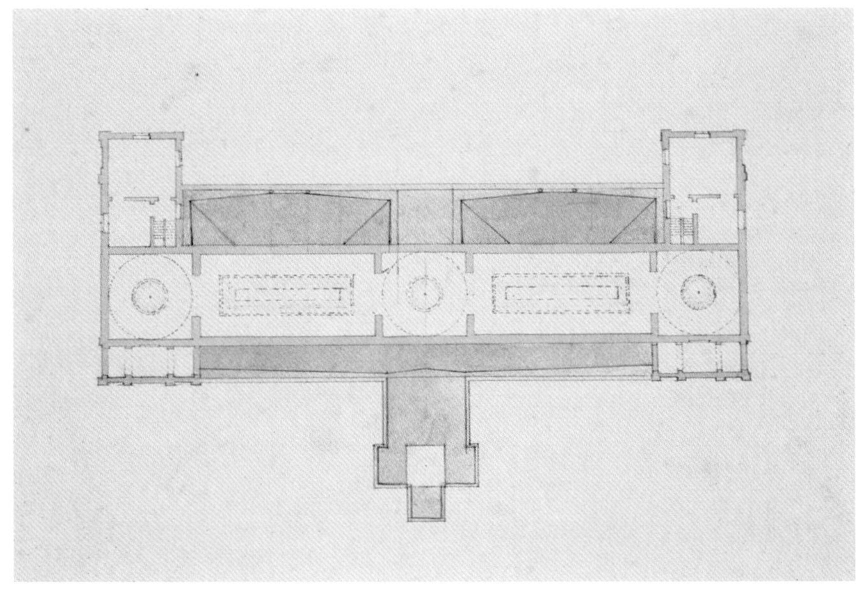

53

Plan of the Upper Storey of the Gallery

G Bailey, GA Underwood, G Basevi or *C Tyrell* 7 August 1811

54
Perspective View of the East Façade with Mausoleum
G Bailey, GA Underwood or *G Basevi* 8 August 1811

55
East Elevation of the Gallery with Mausoleum
Soane Office August 1811

56

Perspective View of the East Façade with Mausoleum

JM Gandy? 1811–12?

The Mausoleum Moves to the West Side of the Gallery: October to November 1811

The foundations of the Gallery were set by Soane on 19 October 1811 presumably following the most recent designs discussed above, all of which show the mausoleum to the east of the Gallery. On 15 November 1811 the 'Private Sittings' book of the College records the decision to move the mausoleum to the west, where it ceased to be a focal point of Soane's desired quadrangle. No reason was given for this change of heart, but Soane had already considered this possibility in his design of 17 July 1811 (No. 41). The matter was obviously much discussed during October and November, and the following drawings can either be dated to this time or related to the issue of re-siting the mausoleum.

57
Perspective View of the West Façade
G Bailey, GA Underwood or *G Basevi* 24 October 1811

58

Perspective View of the West Façade

G Bailey or *GA Underwood* 28 October 1811

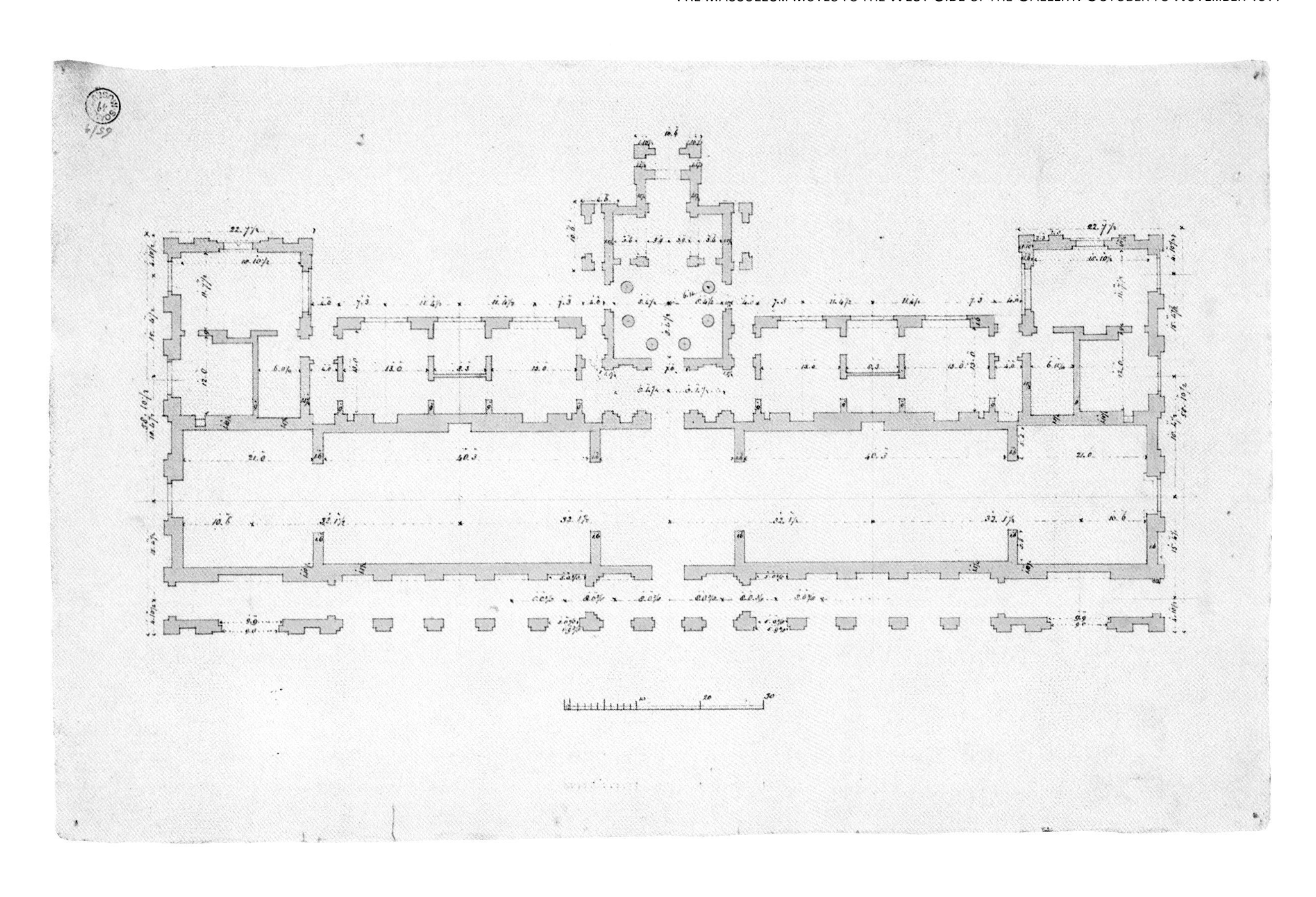

59
Plan of the Gallery
Soane Office 1811?

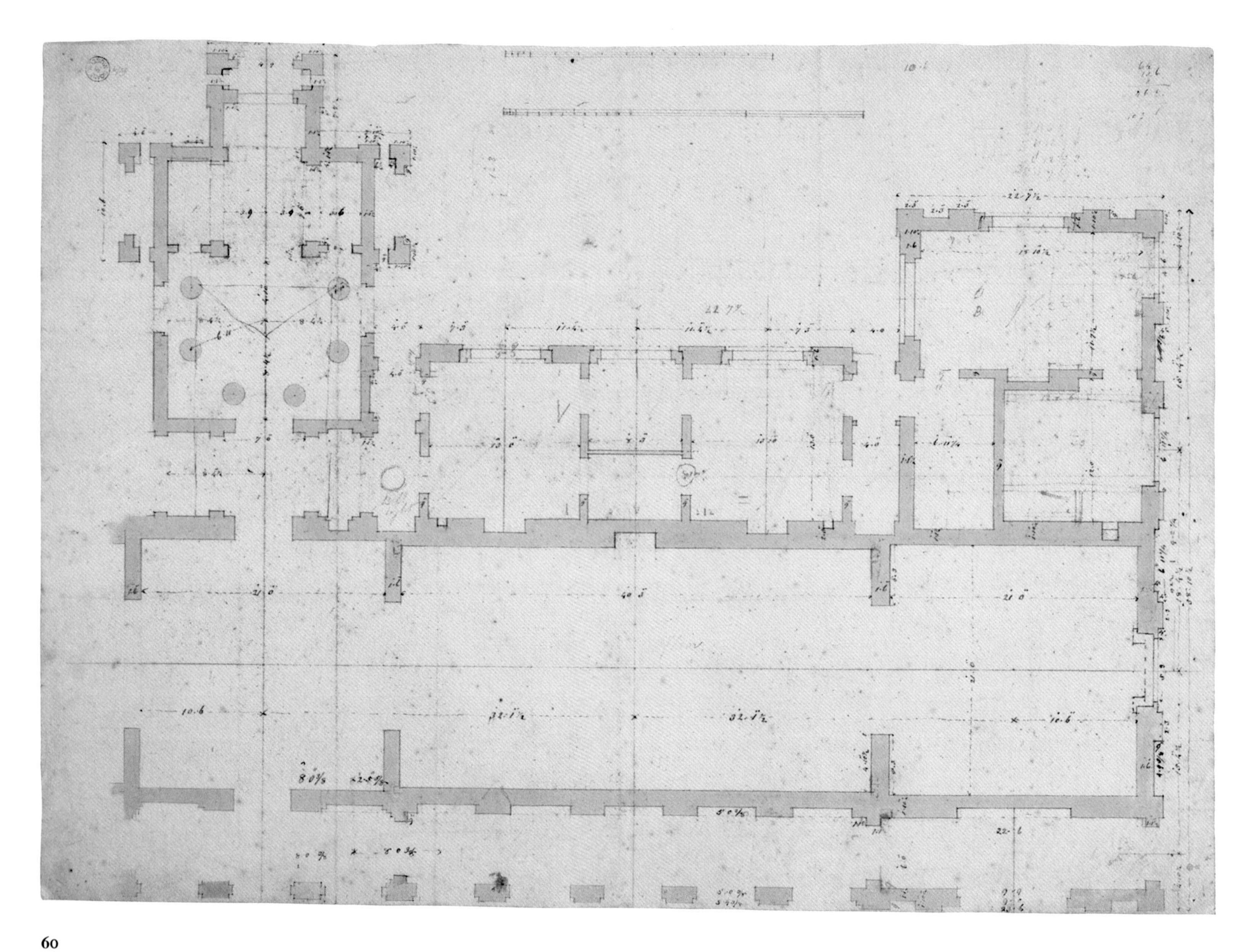

60

Half Plan of the Gallery

Soane Office 1811?

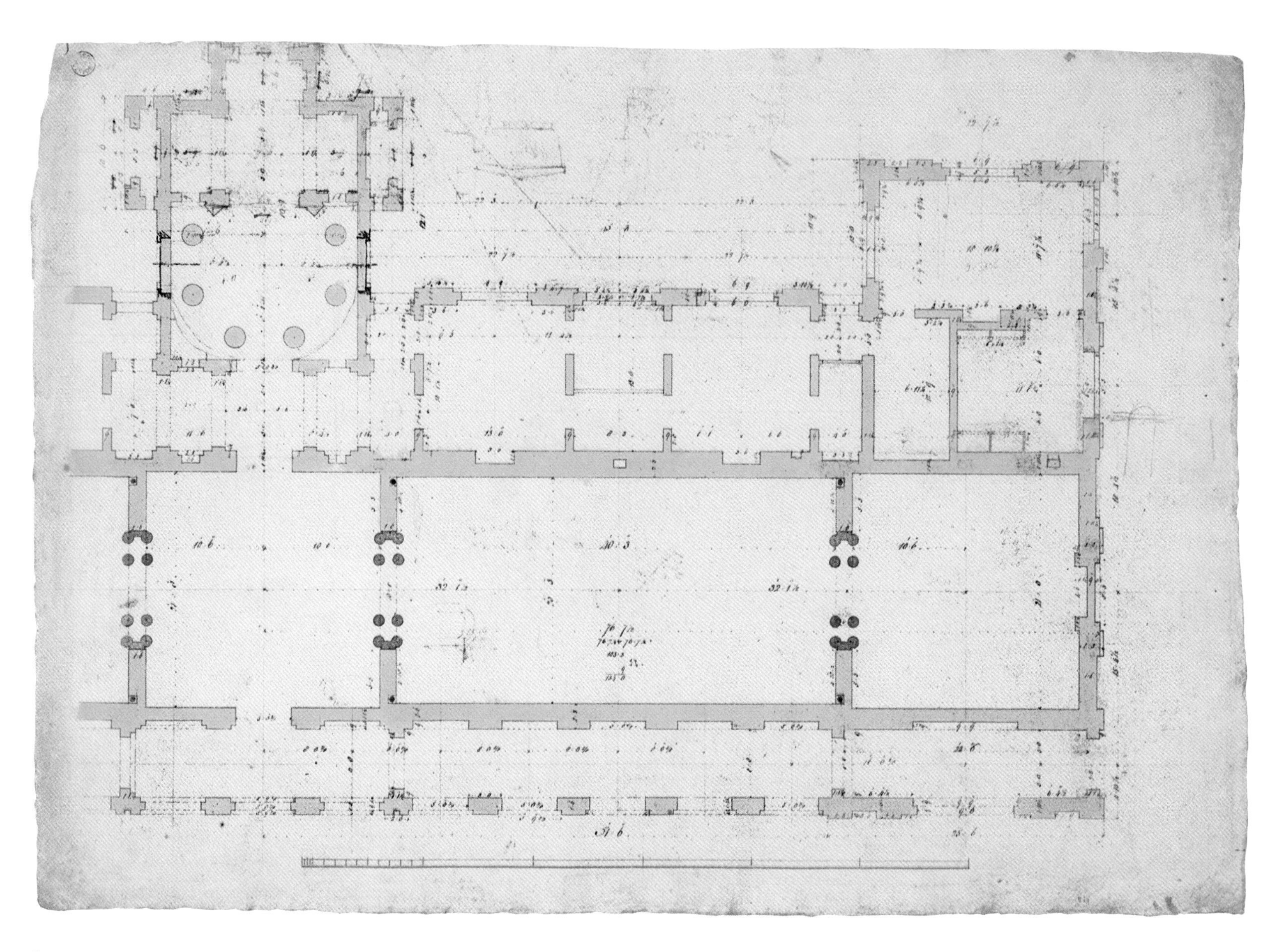

61

Half Plan of the Gallery

Soane Office 1811?

A Porch for the East Façade of the Gallery and Other Designs: October 1811 to April 1812

When on 16 November 1811 the College decided that the mausoleum was to be on the west façade, the question clearly arose how to articulate the centre of the east façade. The following group of drawings, made in early 1812 when the building work was already well under way, show Soane's early ideas for a porch. At this stage he is thinking of a modest single-storey structure, echoing the plan of the mausoleum. This was not built due to a lack of funds. Gandy's composite view of the Gallery of 1823 (No. 116) presents an ideal design for the porch with a tall lantern over the entrance, matching the mausoleum in splendour.

During the same period, while work was progressing, Soane also decided to redesign the Gallery skylights, making them octagonal instead of circular.

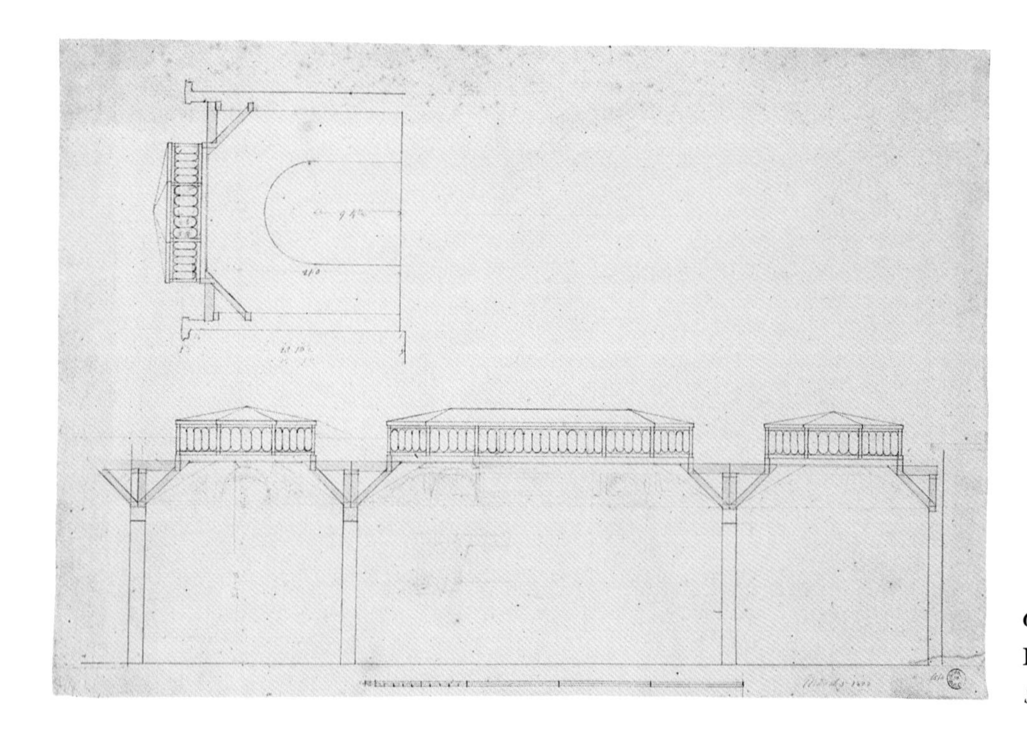

62

Long and Cross Sections Through Gallery

Soane Office 5 March 1812

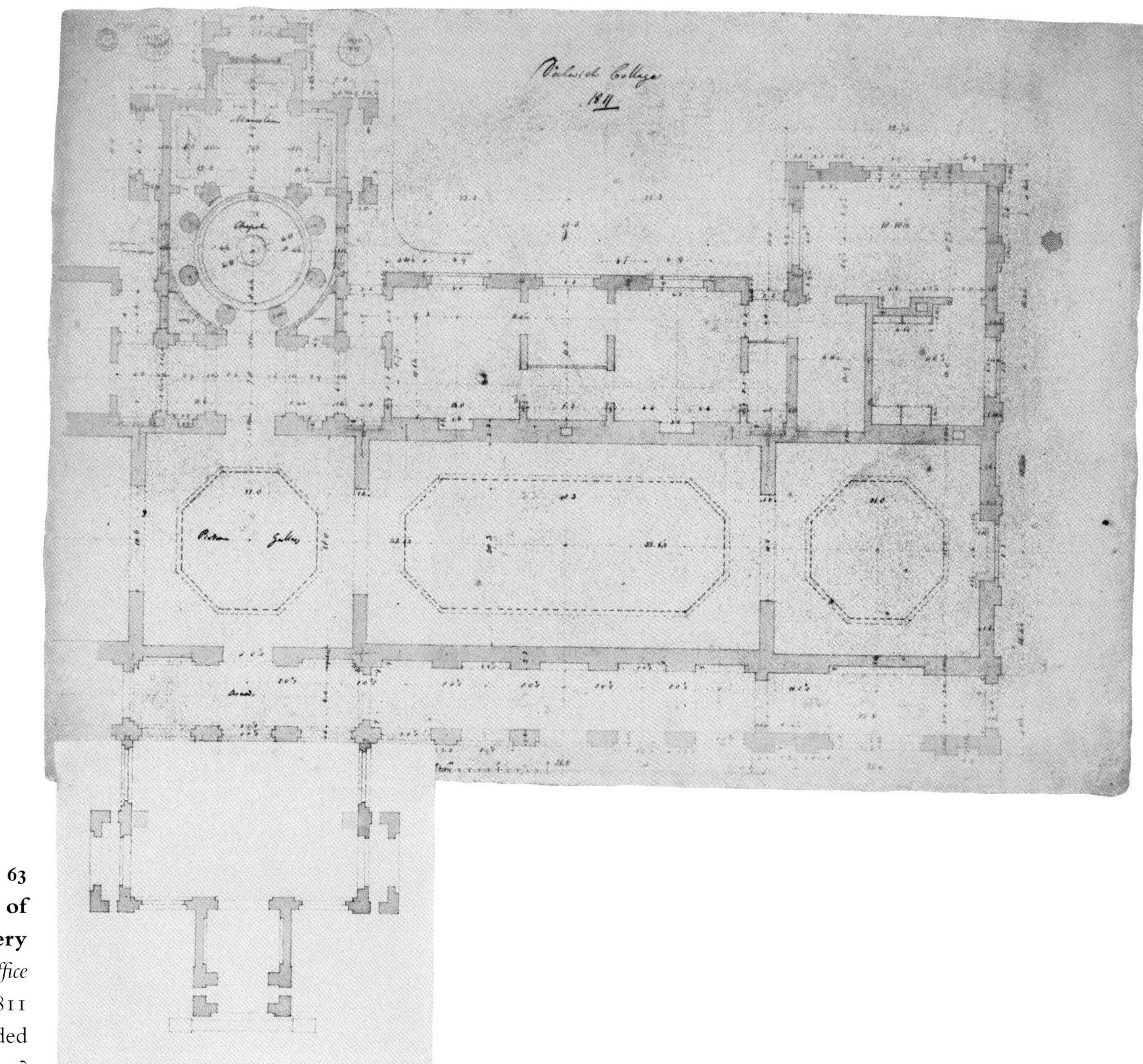

63
Half Plan of the Gallery
Soane Office
1811
flap added
early 1812?

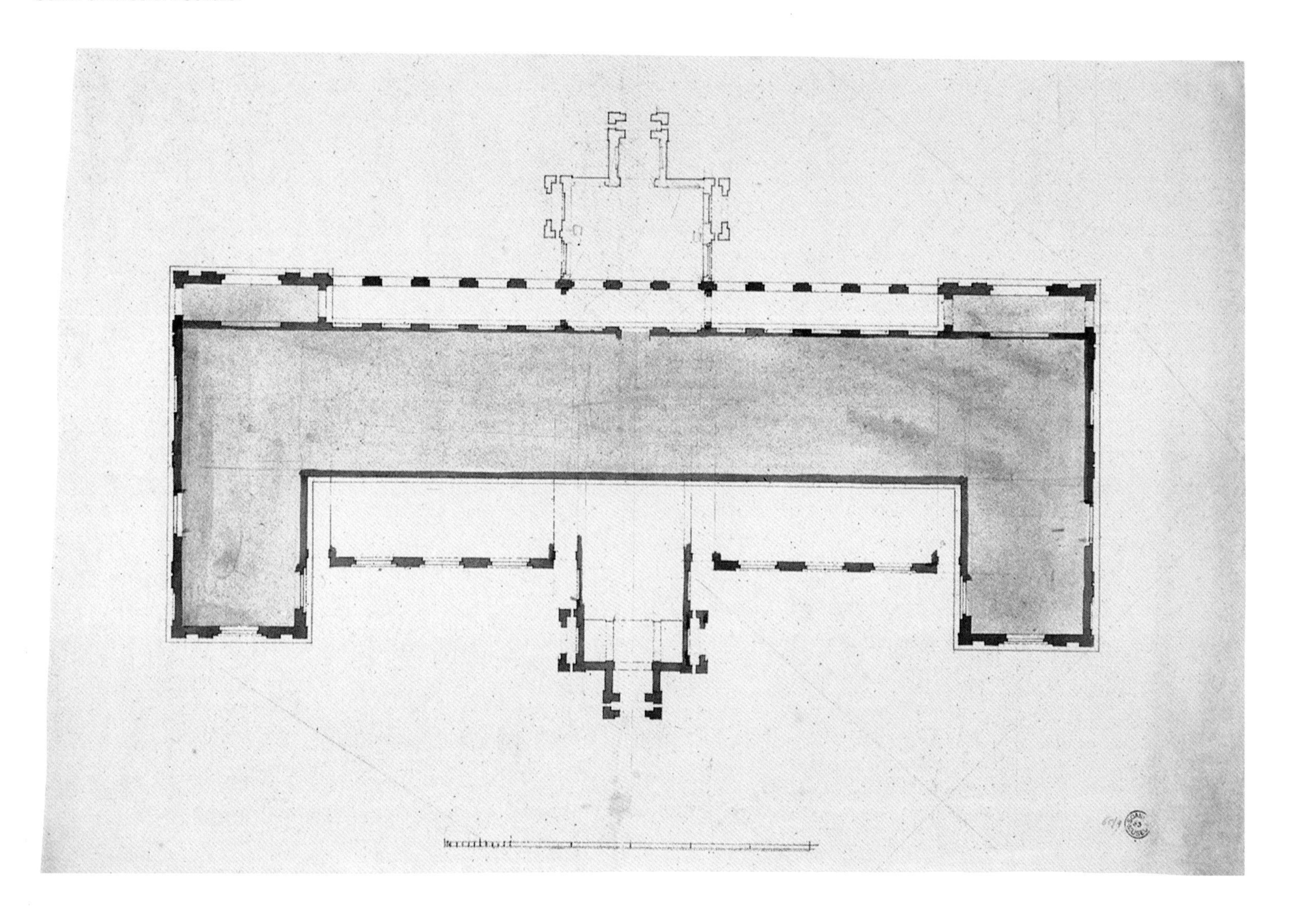

64
Outline Plan of the Gallery
Soane Office early 1812?

65
Perspective View of the East Façade
John Soane? early 1812?

66
Elevation of the East Façade
Soane Office early 1812?

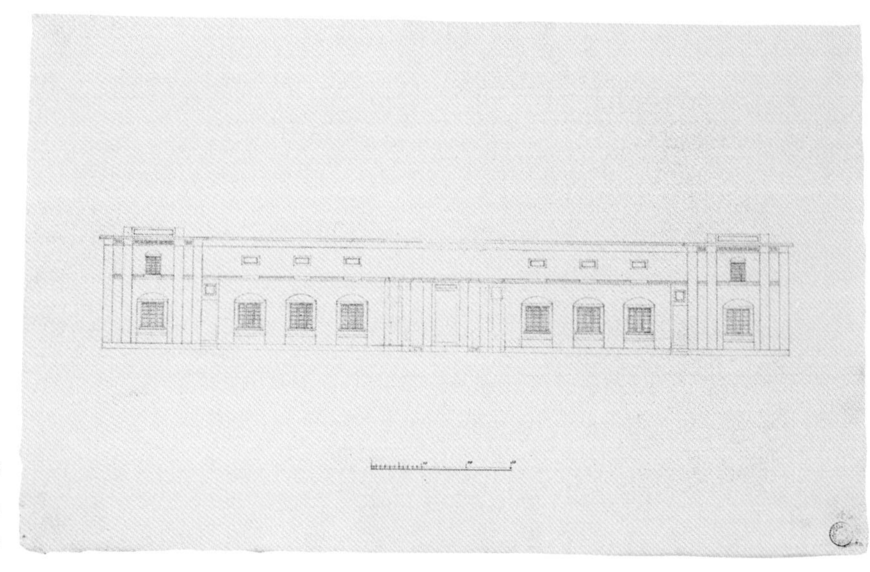

67
Elevation of the West Façade
Soane Office early 1812?

68

Elevations of the East and West Façades

G Bailey, GA Underwood or *G Basevi* 13 April 1812

The North and East Façades of the Gallery: Early 1812

Now that the idea of the east porch had been abandoned, these drawings represent Soane's final designs for the east and north façades. The east façade was built as we see it here, except that the thirteen-bay arcade was only executed in low relief, without its covered loggia. This austere façade projects a formal image appropriate for an art gallery, but Soane's use of brick was regarded by his contemporaries as too poor for so 'noble' a structure. Everywhere in Europe major public buildings were generally of stone, preferably marble, and not humble brick.

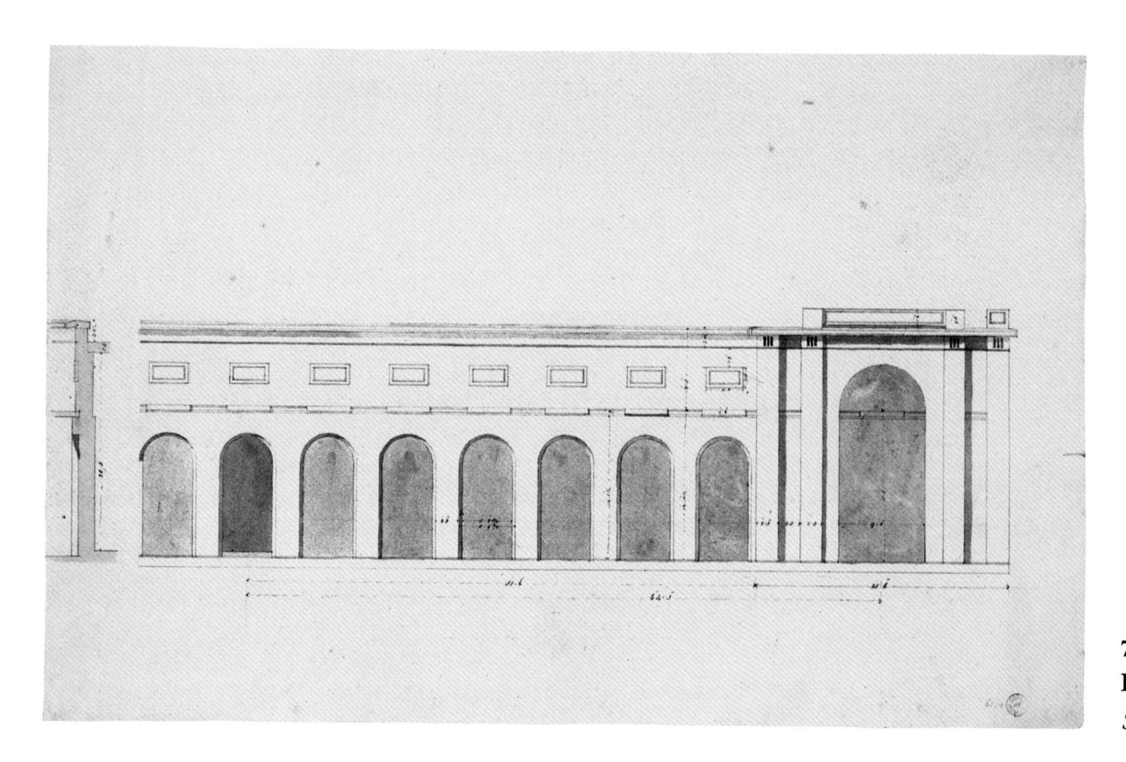

70
Half Elevation of the East Façade
Soane Office 1812?

69

Half Elevation of the East Façade

G Bailey, GA Underwood or *G Basevi* 13 April 1812

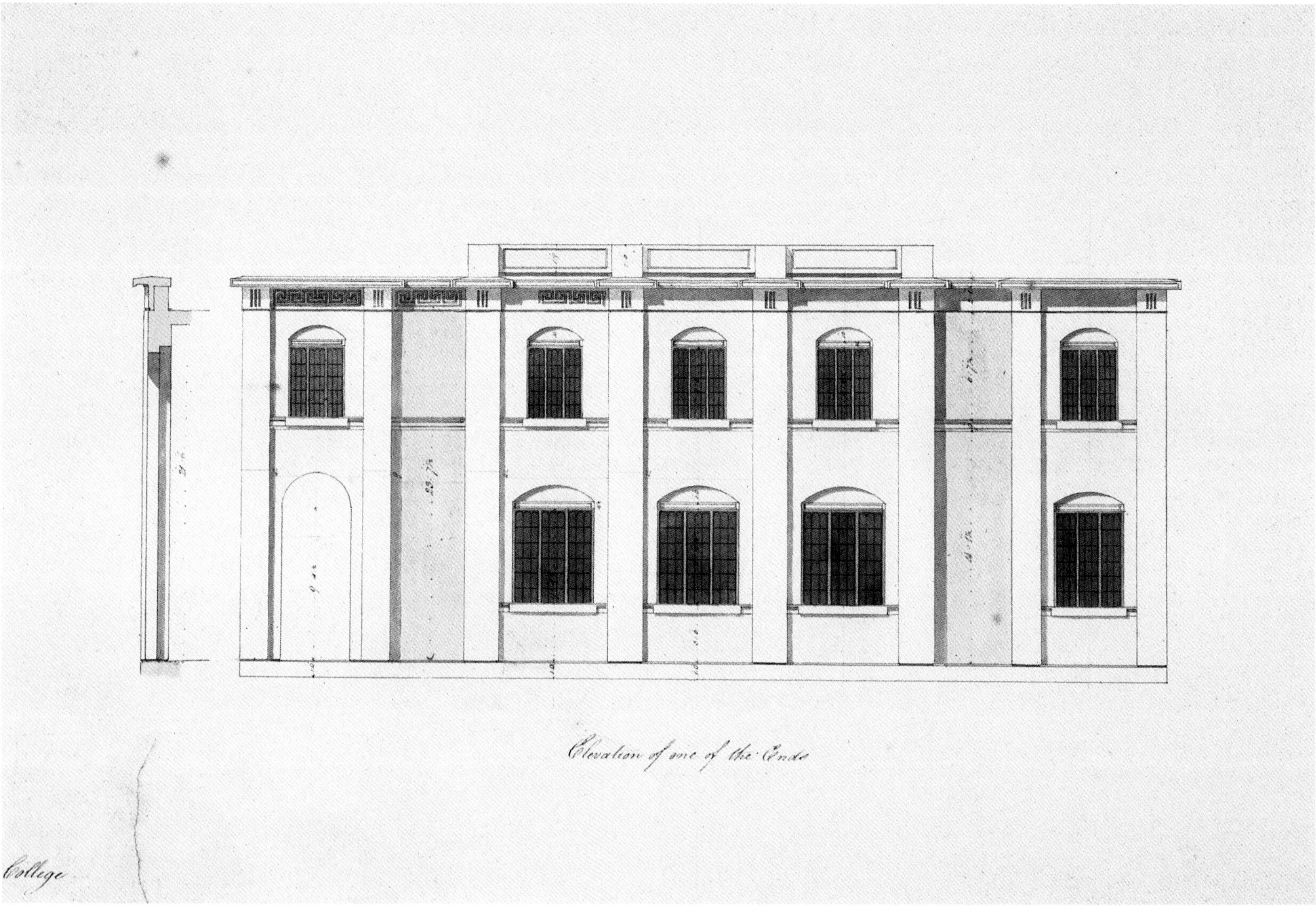

71

Elevation and Section of the North Façade of the Gallery

Soane Office April 1812

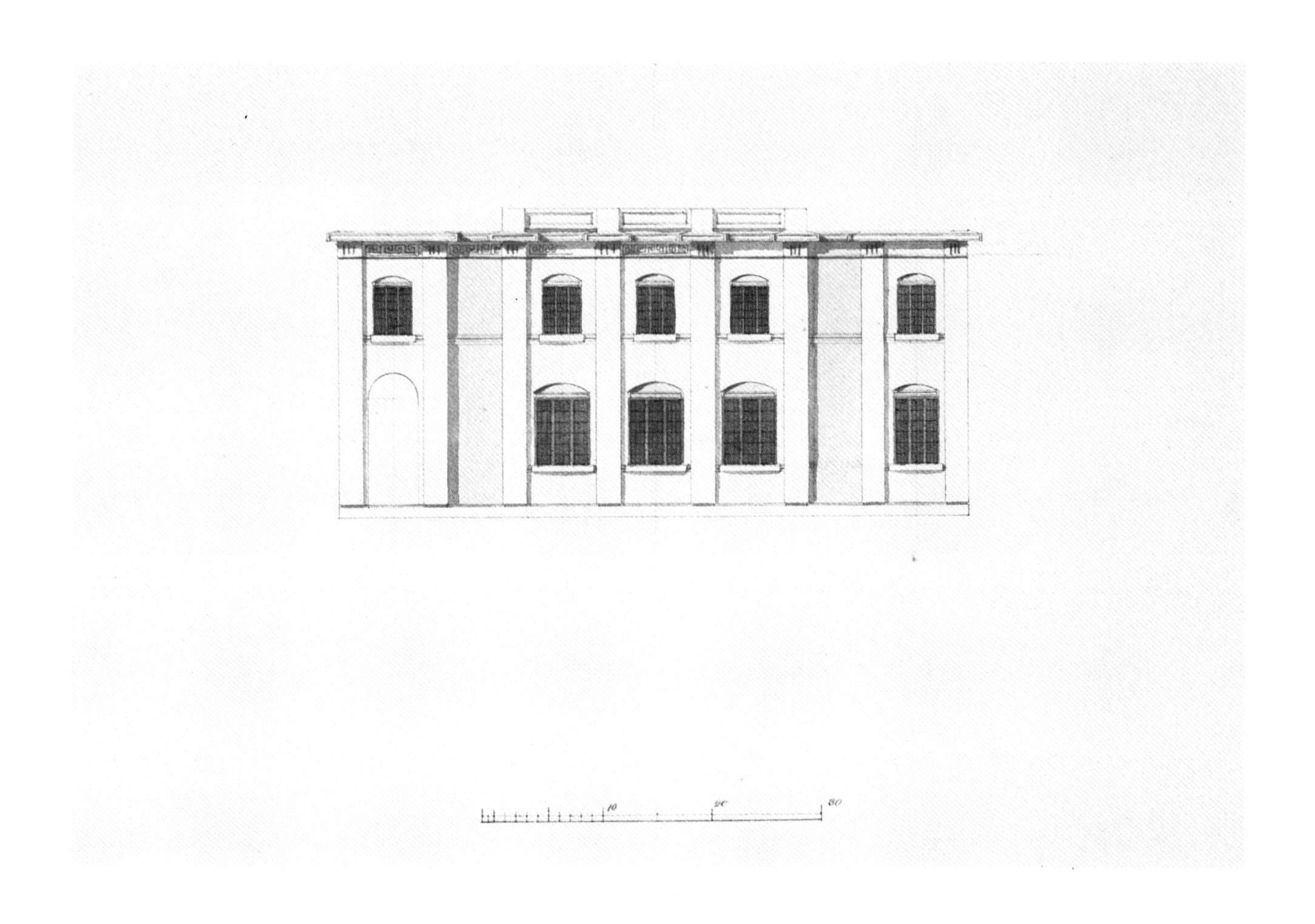

72

Elevation of the North Façade of the Gallery

Soane Office April 1812?

The West Façade and Gallery Roof-Line. Real and Ideal Designs: April to July 1812

When Soane produced his design of 29 April 1812 (No. 73) he had obviously decided on the materials and the essential form of the mausoleum. On 25 May 1812 Soane walked out to Dulwich to set out its plinth. Building progress views of the Gallery show that during May and June the whole of the west façade, including the mausoleum, was well under construction (see Nos. 90 and 93–7). Yet at this time his office was still producing new designs for the mausoleum and almshouse windows. Some of these (especially the measured drawings of details like Nos. 74 and 89) were clearly for the final design. However it seems that from May 1812 Soane spent some time designing elements – richly decorated and in costly materials – that he knew would never be built. This ideal design process (which can be traced through Nos. 78–83 below) runs in parallel with the real design process and results not in a building but a large exhibition watercolour – JM Gandy's romanticised view of the west façade, shown at the Royal Academy in 1813 (No. 82).

74
Elevation of the Lantern
Soane Office May 1812?

73
Section and Elevation of the Mausoleum
G Basevi 29 April 1812

75
Perspective View of the Mausoleum
G Basevi 11 May 1812

76
Perspective View of the Mausoleum
Soane Office May 1812?

77

Elevation of the West Façade

Soane Office May 1812?

78

Perspective of the Mausoleum with a Plan of the Gallery and Views of the East and West Façades Inserted Below

R Chantrell or G Basevi

23 May 1812

79
Perspective View of the Mausoleum
Soane Office May 1812?

80

Perspective View of the Mausoleum

Soane Office May 1812?

81

Perspective View of the Mausoleum

R Chantrell 11 June 1812

82

Perspective View of the West Façade

JM Gandy probably second half of 1812

83
Perspective View of the West Façade
JM Gandy? probably 1812

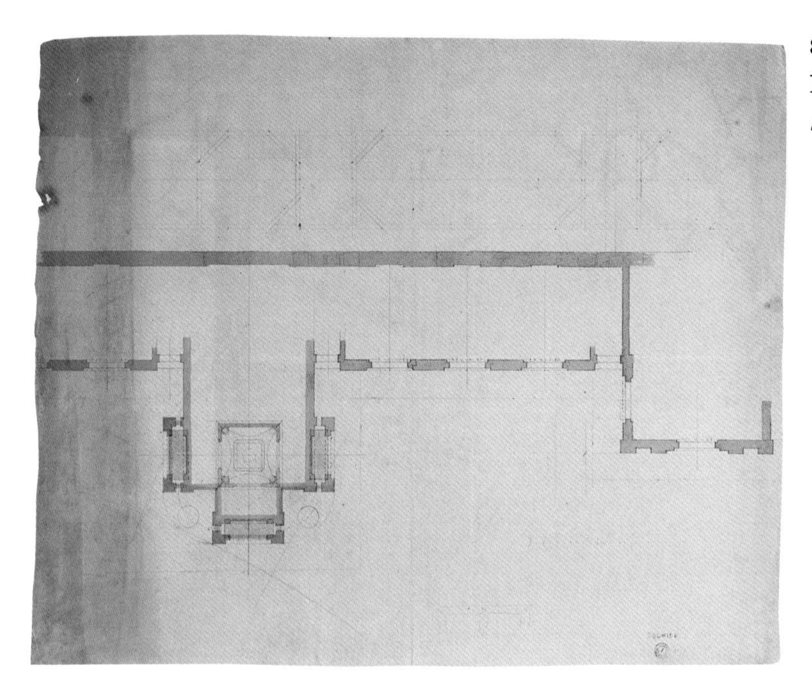

84
Plan of Half the Top Storey of the Gallery
Soane Office May 1812?

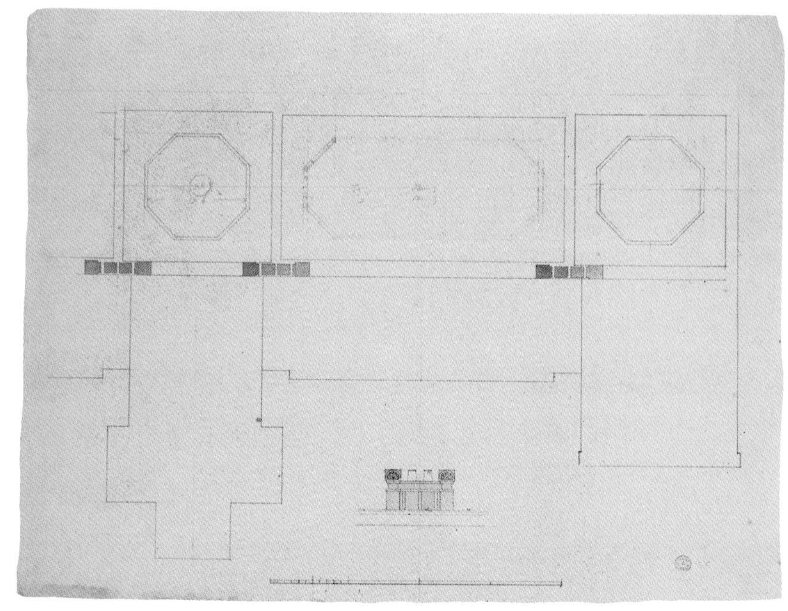

86
Line Plan and Section of Half of the Gallery
Soane Office May 1812?

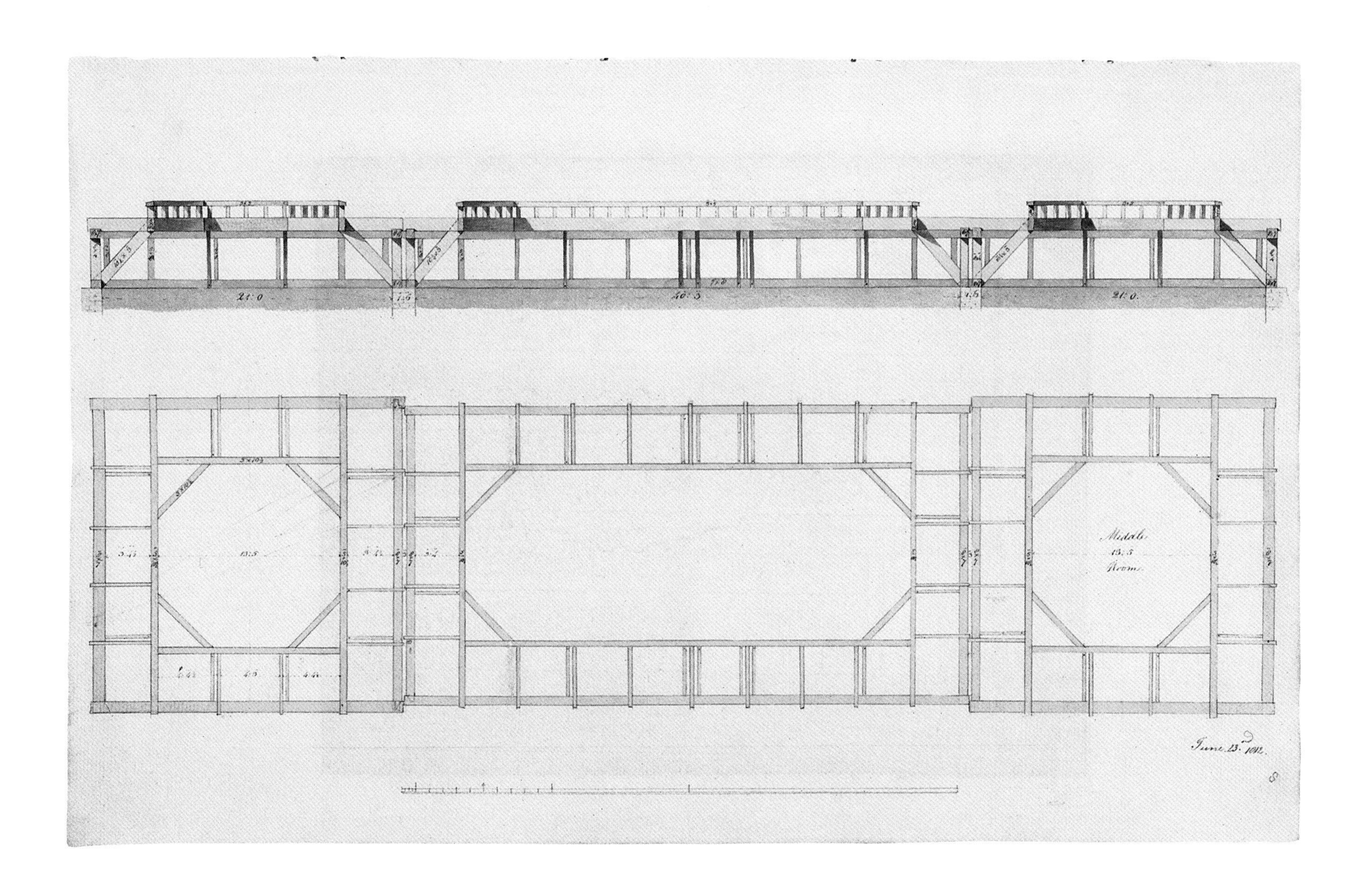

85

Plan and Section of the Framework for the Gallery Vaults

C Tyrell, G Basevi or *R Chantrell* 13 June 1812

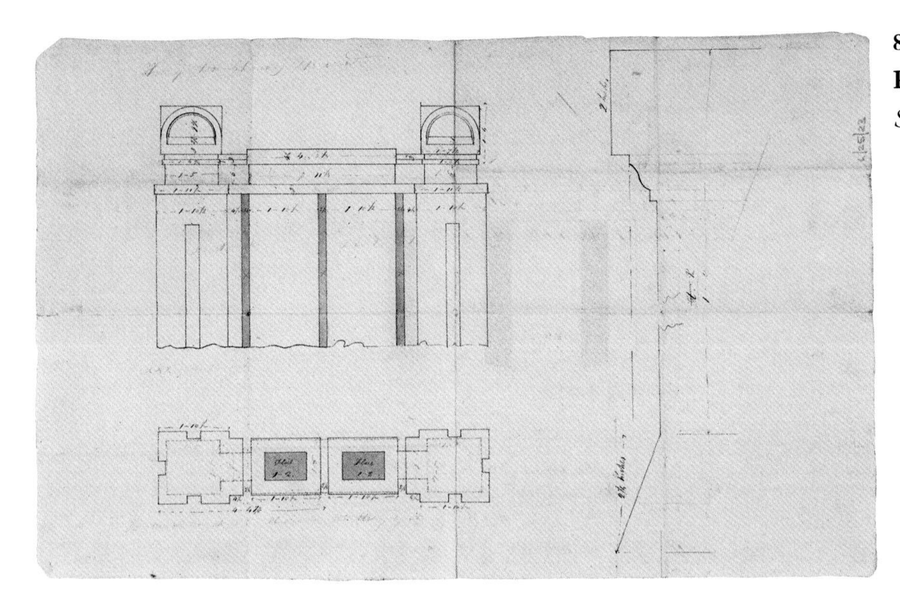

87
Plan and Elevation of the Chimneys: Recto
Soane Office May 1812?

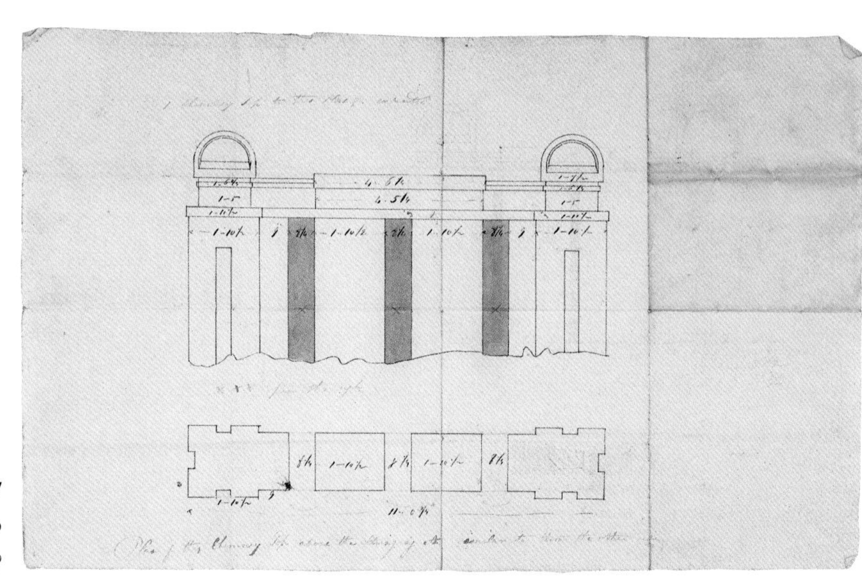

87
Plan and Elevation of the Chimneys: Verso
Soane Office May 1812?

88

Elevation of West Façade Chimney

C Tyrell 1812

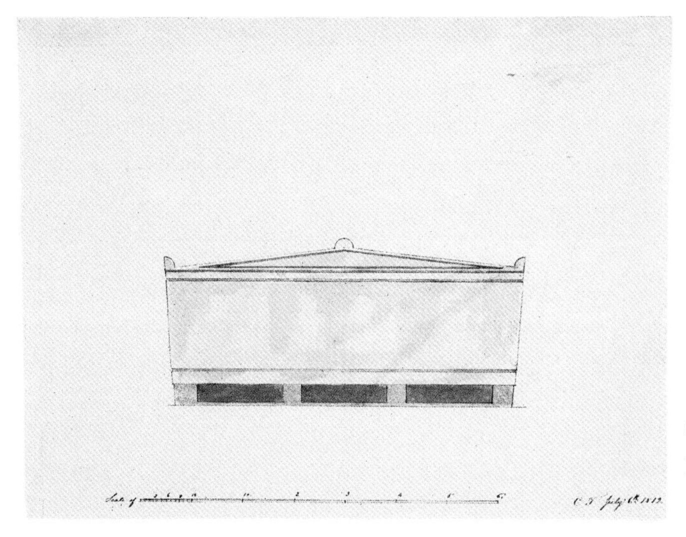

89

Elevation of a Sarcophagus

C Tyrell 6 July 1812

The Building in Progress: May to September 1812

The following progress views made at Dulwich are all bound in a single volume, dated 1812, at the Soane Museum. Some of them are signed by Soane's pupils, including George Basevi, Robert Chantrell and Charles Tyrell; others are dated and can be attributed by reference to Soane's Day Book. George Basevi formally enrolled at Soane's office in December 1810 and was joined a month later by Robert Tyrell; their progress views at Dulwich were among their first external assignments. Soane regarded these site visits as a way for young architects to learn about the mechanics of building.

These progress views are especially fascinating as a record of building technology at this date. Heavy materials such as timber would be brought to site by horse and cart, and sheds were erected on site for the building materials that needed protection from the elements. Every part of the building site is recorded by Soane's pupils: the scaffolding made up of poles and hemp ropes; the mounds of sand and lime; the stacks of planks and timber beams for rafters.

The final accounts of the workmen employed by Soane at Dulwich are also preserved at the Soane Museum. Often more than one firm was employed in what would seem to be the same trade. The stonemason, Thomas Grundy, was paid £1,243 6s 6d to supply and carve the Portland stone elements of the Gallery and mausoleum and the masons, John Day and Son received £553 9s 5d for additional work. Underwood & Co, specialist manufacturers of metal sashes, supplied the windows and yellow glass for the mausoleum, at a cost of £46 3s 8d, while the painter and glazier William Watson was paid £373 3s 2d. The bricklayer JH Lee charged £2,804 3s 3d; the carpenters, Martyr and Son and W Tristram, were paid £2,343 7s 2d and £590 10d respectively. The plumbers, William Good and Lancelot Burton (whose lead melting aparatus is illustrated here), were paid £777 16s 3d and £385 14s 3d respectively. The plasterers, J and J Bayley and William Rothwel, received £392 5s 10d and £1 2s 6d. The slaters W and I Sharp received £39 13s 1d for their work, and Stevens and Wedd, ironmonger, were paid £13 7s 6d. The smiths, T Russell, J Mitchel and Co. and T Hearsey, received £49 18s 2d, £21 2s 4d and £9 9s for their labour. The building work and accounts were supervised by one of Soane's favourite Clerk of Works, James Cook, who was paid £68 8s, as well as by Henry Harrison (paid £40 19s 9d) and Walter Payne (£10 10s). Catering costs for the builders came to £24 14s 9d. The total cost of the work, completed by 1814, was £9,778 14s 11d, substantially less than Soane's estimate made on 5 August 1811 of £11,270.

When the exterior of the building was completed in September 1812, Messrs Bolton and Watt's steam-heating system was installed at a cost of £270. This was not a success: a report dated 26 July 1813 found that the pipes leaked, causing dry rot, and that the steam boiler was a fire risk. The boiler was eventually re-sited in a room next to the College kitchen, where it is shown in Charles Barry Junior's 1858 plan (No. 135).

From 1813, Soane appears to have handed over the supervision of the building work to George Tappen, the College surveyor since 1805. Soane's copy of Tappen's book *Professional Observations on the Architecture of the Principal Ancient and Modern Buildings in France and Italy*, was presented to him by the author in 1807 and is heavily annotated in Soane's hand. The paintings were installed in the Gallery in September 1814.

90

The West Façade and Mausoleum Under Construction

G Basevi 29 May 1812

91
The Gallery Interior Under Construction
R Chantrell 29 May 1812

92

The Gallery Interior Under Construction

R Chantrell or *G Basevi* 3 June 1812

93
Construction View of the Mausoleum
G Basevi 3 June 1812

94
Bird's Eye View of the Gallery and Mausoleum
R Chantrell
13 June 1812

95

The West Façade Under Construction

R Chantrell 19 June 1812

96
The Mausoleum from Inside the South Almshouse
R Chantrell
19 June 1812

97
The Enfilade and Mausoleum Under Construction
R Chantrell or *R Basevi* 29 June 1812

98
The Enfilade Under Construction
G Basevi or *C Tyrell* 6 July 1812

99
The West Façade Under Construction
G Basevi or C Tyrell 6 July 1812

100

Interior View of the Almshouses and Mausoleum

C Tyrell 7 July 1812

101

The Mausoleum from the Gallery Roof

R Chantrell 28 July 1812

102

The Enfilade Under Construction

C Tyrell 30 July 1812

103
The Enfilade and Mausoleum Under Construction
Soane Office 1812

104
The Interior of the Mausoleum Under Construction
R Chantrell 29 July or 10 August 1812

105
One of Soane's Pupils Sketching
Soane Office July 1812

106

The West Façade

Soane Office 1812

107

The East Façade

GA Underwood or *G Basevi* 12 August 1812

108
Plumbers' Lead Being Melted
G Basevi 13 August 1812

109

The West Façade from the South

R Chantrell 13 August 1812

110

The West Façade from Gallery Road

R Chantrell 12 September 1812

Royal Academy Lecture Drawings: 1815

In 1802 Soane was elected a full Royal Academician and in 1806 he succeeded his master George Dance as Professor of Architecture. Unlike Dance, who had not given a single lecture, Soane presented an entire series, engaging his office to produce the illustrations. Over 1,000 coloured drawings survive, covering every class of building and the work of many famous architects. The subject of his twelfth Royal Academy lecture in 1815 was 'a thorough knowledge of construction, and of the nature and quality of the different materials applicable in the formation of buildings of different descriptions, together with the most durable, substantial, and economical modes of applying them'. These five large-scale copies of progress views are all associated with that lecture, though in the event Soane showed only three of them.

The text of this lecture offers Soane's best explanation of the function of the progress view: 'by attending the progress of buildings and by making drawings of them in their different stages of progress, the student will not only attain great skill in the mechanism of buildings, but at the same time discover many effects of light and shade which a close examination of nature can only give. By this mode of study he will acquire a facility and freedom in drawing, and at the same time observe and treasure up in his mind a variety of forms and ideas that the same buildings when finished would not convey. The young artist must not stop with making such drawings: he must at the same time consider and make his remarks on every part of the construction, and if after the work is completed, defects appear in the building, he will be enabled to account for them, and what is still more important, he will be able eventually to avoid similar ones in his works.'

111

Royal Academy Lecture Drawing:
The West Façade of the Gallery Under Construction
Soane Office *c.*1815

112
Royal Academy Lecture Drawing:
The West Façade of the Gallery Under Construction
Soane Office *c.* 1815

113
Royal Academy Lecture Drawing: View of the Gallery and Mausoleum Under Construction
Soane Office c. 1815

114
The West Façade Under Construction
Soane Office *c.* 1815

115
The West Façade Under Construction
Soane Office *c.* 1815

Gandy's Composite View of 1823

Soane exhibited designs for Dulwich at the Royal Academy on five different occasions, in 1811, 1812, 1813, 1815 and 1823. There is always an element of conjecture when matching Royal Academy exhibition catalogues with the surviving watercolours of Soane's office, but there are reasonable candidates for the first three of these exhibitions: No. 29 in 1811; No. 56 in 1812; and No. 82 in 1813. The 'Design for a Mausoleum' exhibited in 1815 cannot be identified. All these watercolours are by Gandy and they all show a building different from that finally built. It is difficult to be sure in every case, but some of these were known by Soane to be unrealisable, ideal designs even when they were exhibited.

The last view of Dulwich exhibited at the Royal Academy was the 'Architectural Study' of the 'Picture Gallery and Mausoleum' listed in the 1823 catalogue – Gandy's famous composite watercolour. This time the impetus appears to have been Revd T F Dibdin's attack on Soane's architecture in *The Museum* (a journal which appeared briefly between 1822–24), which described the Gallery thus: 'What a thing – what a creature it is! A maeso-gothic, semi-arabic, moro-spanish, an anglico-norman – a 'what you will' production! It hath no compeer ... It has all the merit and emphatic distinction of being *unique* ... [and] ... delightfully monstrous'. Though Soane refers specifically to Dibdin in his title, there is no obvious way in which this composite image addresses these criticisms. The only clear message is contained in the titles of the individual parts. For example, in three of them Soane presents a new idea, related to the elevation of 13 April 1812 (No. 68) but with the east porch exactly like another mausoleum, and calls it his 'original design'. He presumably means that this is his favoured design. Views of the building as executed – which are now examined as priceless records – are referred to contemptuously as showing its 'present unfinished and altered state'. Various drawings are included in this group which are obviously related to Gandy's watercolour.

117
Ideal View of the East Façade of the Gallery
JM Gandy *c.* 1823

116

'Mausoleum and Picture Gallery with God's Gift College, Dulwich'

JM Gandy 1823

118

Ideal View of the Gallery from the South East

Soane Office *c.* 1823

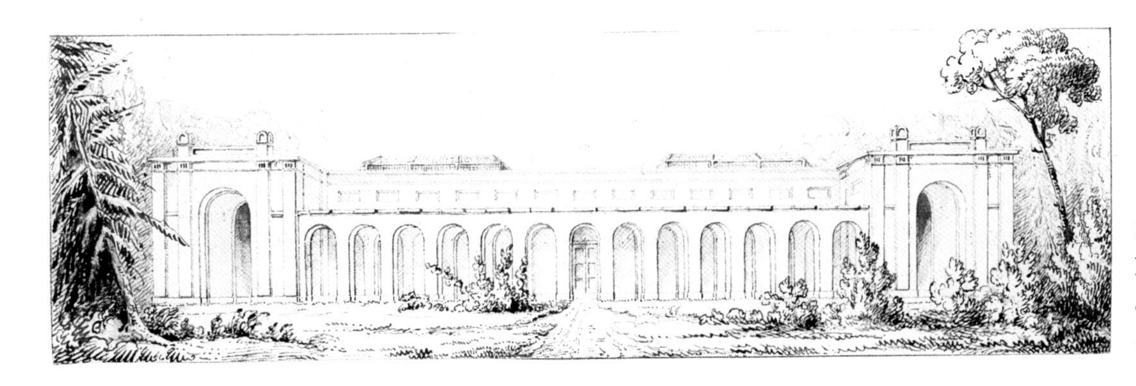

119
Perspective View of the East Façade of the Gallery with an Arcade
CJ Richardson *c.* 1828

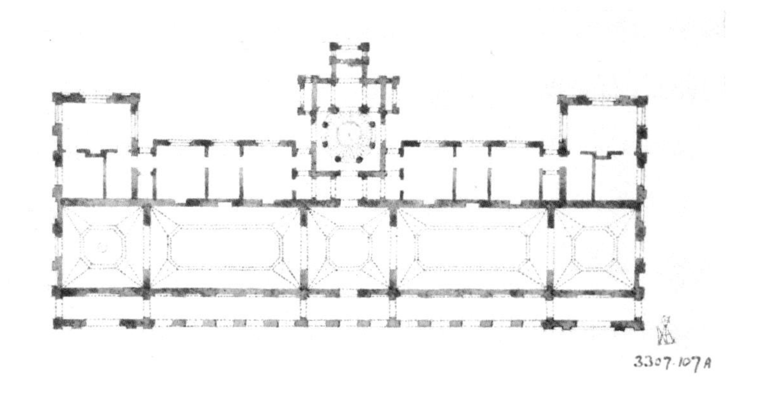

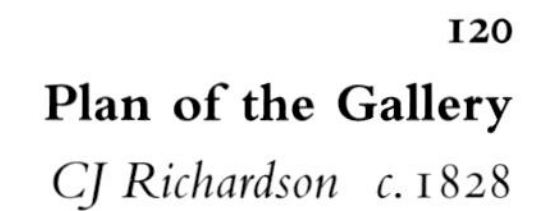

120
Plan of the Gallery
CJ Richardson *c.* 1828

121
Perspective View of the West Façade of the Gallery
CJ Richardson *c.* 1828

George Tappen's Work at Dulwich College: 1805 to 1830

In 1813, the supervision of the completion of the new Gallery was entrusted to George Tappen (1771–1830), the 'Architect and Surveyor to the Governors of Dulwich College Estate' from 1805 to his death in 1830. The College 'Private Sittings' book for 24 July 1814 mentions a sum of £900 for the completion to Tappen's design of the Poor Sisters Apartments in the 'new west wing', as the Gallery building was called. By 1815 this work had been finished at a cost of £845. At the same meeting, on 24 July 1814, Tappen was commissioned to build new stables and a coach house; £650 and 'the materials of the old stable in front of the picture gallery' were set aside for this purpose. In 1815–16 Tappen added a 'New Porch' at the south end of the Gallery and the walled 'Fore Court' seen in Nos. 123 and 135. In preparation for the public opening in 1817, he laid the green oil cloth floor in the Gallery, installed the brass rail to protect the pictures, carried out some repairs to the mausoleum and skylights, and improved the almshouses.

Between 1820 and 1829 Tappen refurbished the south and west ranges of the College. Now that the old women were housed in the Gallery block, the 'old' west wing could be entirely given over to the school: Tappen's proposal (Nos. 124–5) marks rooms for two masters and the boys' sick ward, with the boys' dining room and two dormitories above. The Master and Warden were still lodged in the south-west corner of the south range of the College; on its ground floor, Tappen shows a large new kitchen, a dining room and butlers' rooms, as well as wine and beer cellars, with an ample library and living quarters above. It is also almost certainly Tappen who added an aisle to the south side of the chapel at this time, bringing its façade into line with the newly refurbished Master's lodgings. It is also probable that Tappen built Gallery Cottage, which still stands to the south of the Gallery.

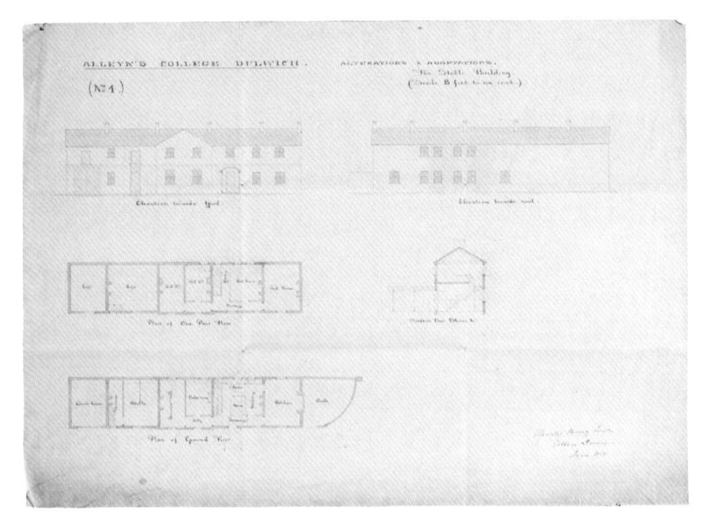

122 Plan and Elevation of the Stable Building
Charles Barry Junior June 1858

123 The Gallery and 'New Porch' 1815–16 *c.*1820

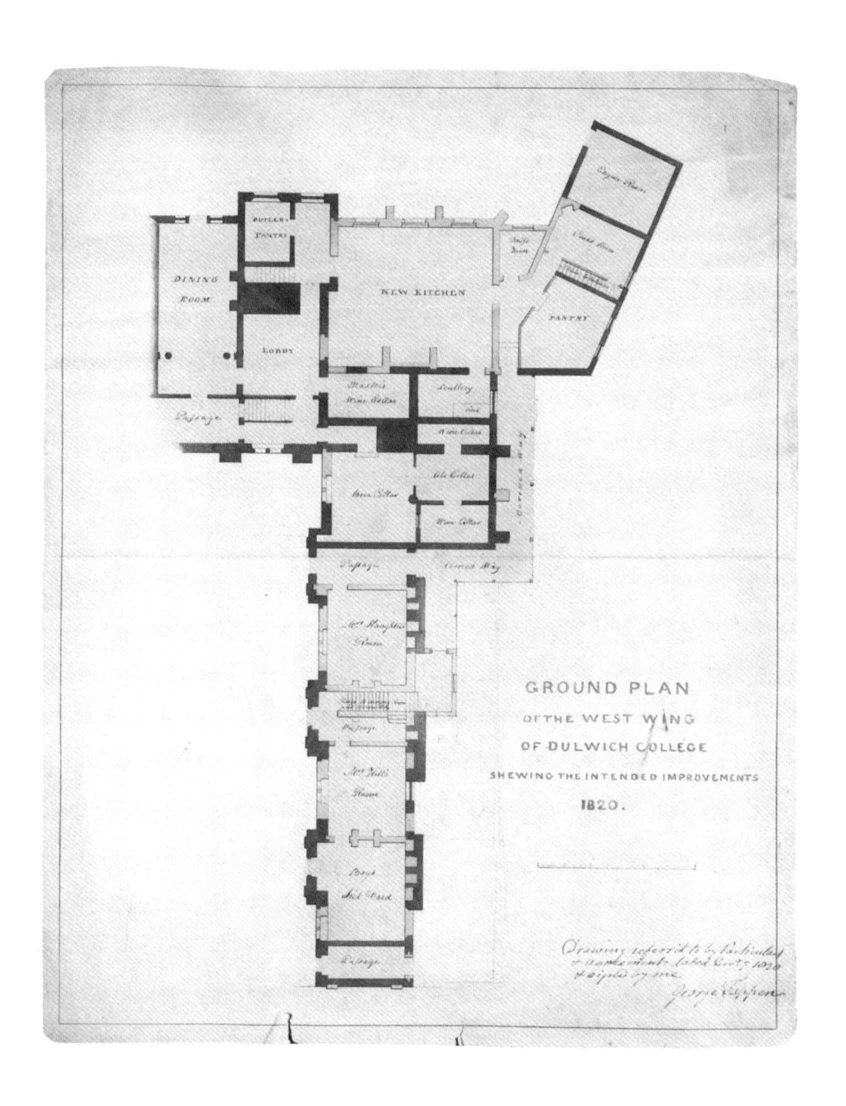

124

Ground Plan of the West Wing of Dulwich College

George Tappen 1820

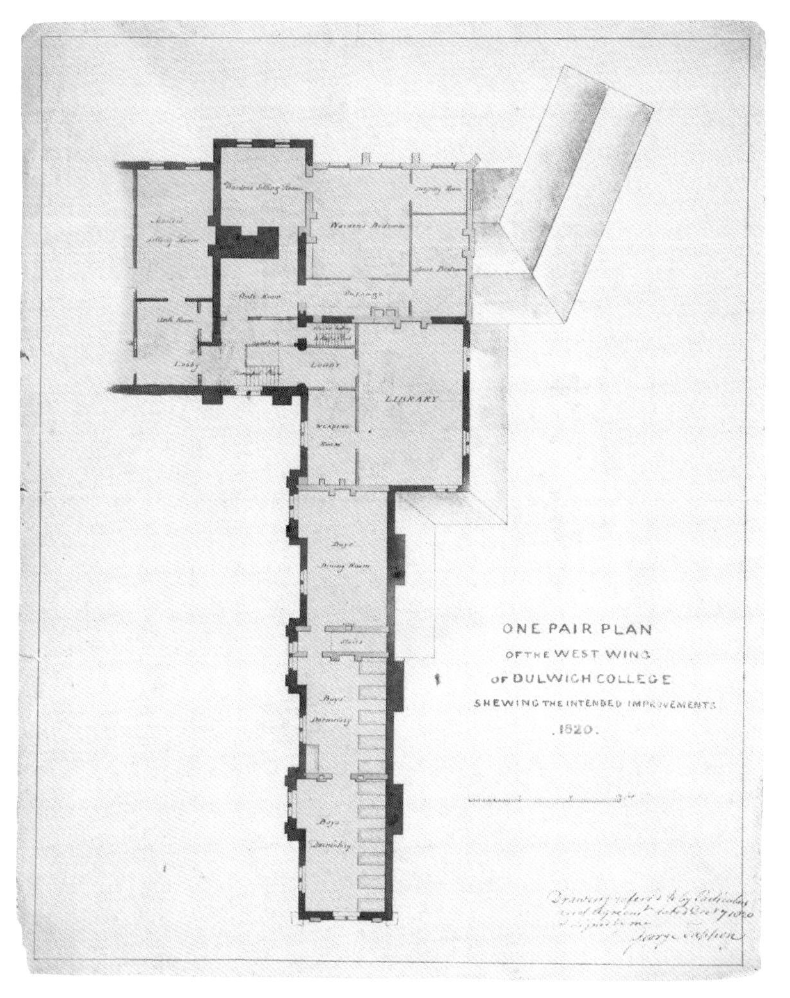

125

First Floor Plan of the West Wing of Dulwich College

George Tappen 1820

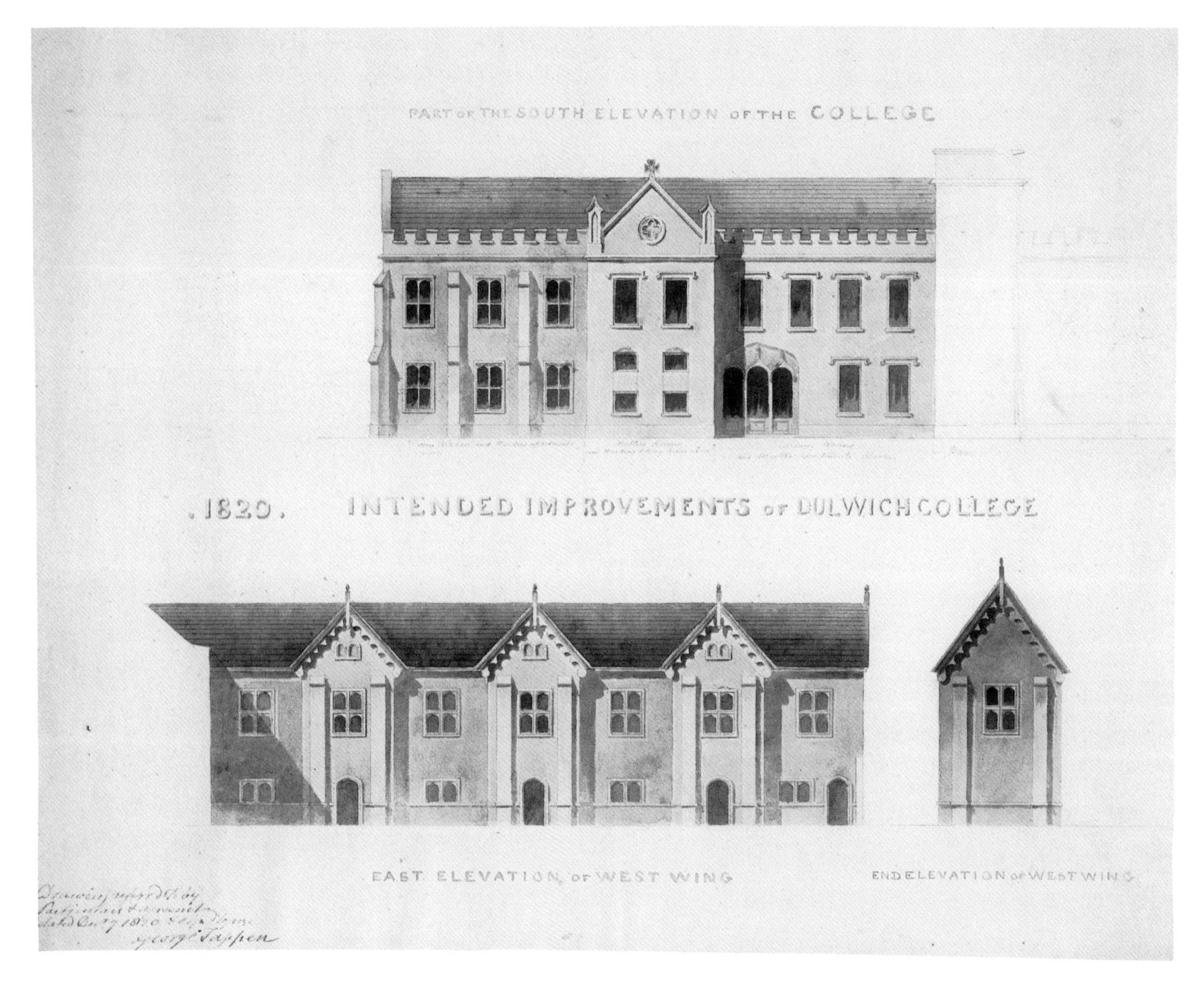

126 South Elevation of the South Range and East Elevation of the West Range of Dulwich College
George Tappen 1820

127
View of Dulwich College from the North
J Rogers after *N Wittock* 1829

128
The Gallery and College Chapel from the South
c. 1840

Sir Charles Barry's Work at Dulwich College: 1831 to 1858

Sir Charles Barry (1795–1860), the future creator of the Houses of Parliament, was appointed architect and surveyor to the Governors of Dulwich College Estate in 1831, after Tappen's death. At the College he was responsible for the remodelling of the east wing and the addition of a block of three rooms to the west of Tappen's west wing. All this work was executed between 1831 and 1846 in the fashionable Gothic Revival style. Nothing survives of his east wing (except the series of chimneys along the saddle of the roof), but prints and drawings show an ornate block with a two-storey oriel window at its north end and crowned with a ring of gables and finials. An idea of its appearance can also be gained from the surviving west extension, which includes the present Board Room.

In 1841 Sir Charles Barry designed and built the nearby Grammar School, still visible on the corner of Gallery Road and Burbage Road.

130 **Dulwich College from the North** *Rock & Co.* 1849

131
The Old Grammar School, Dulwich
Rock & Co 1849

129
Dulwich College from the North
From *Braley's Surrey* 1846

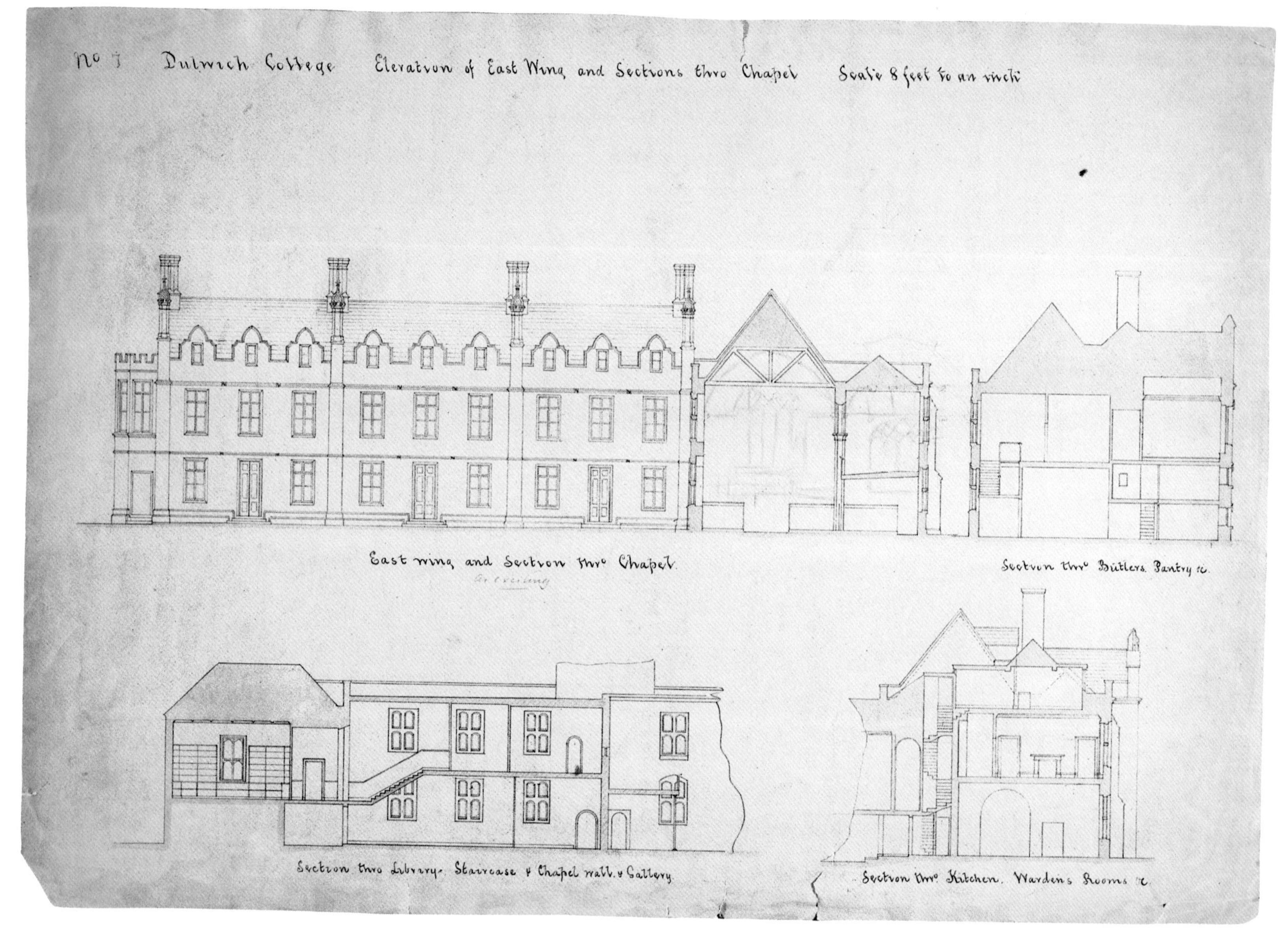

132

West Elevation of the East Wing and Section Through South Range of the College

Charles Barry Junior 1858

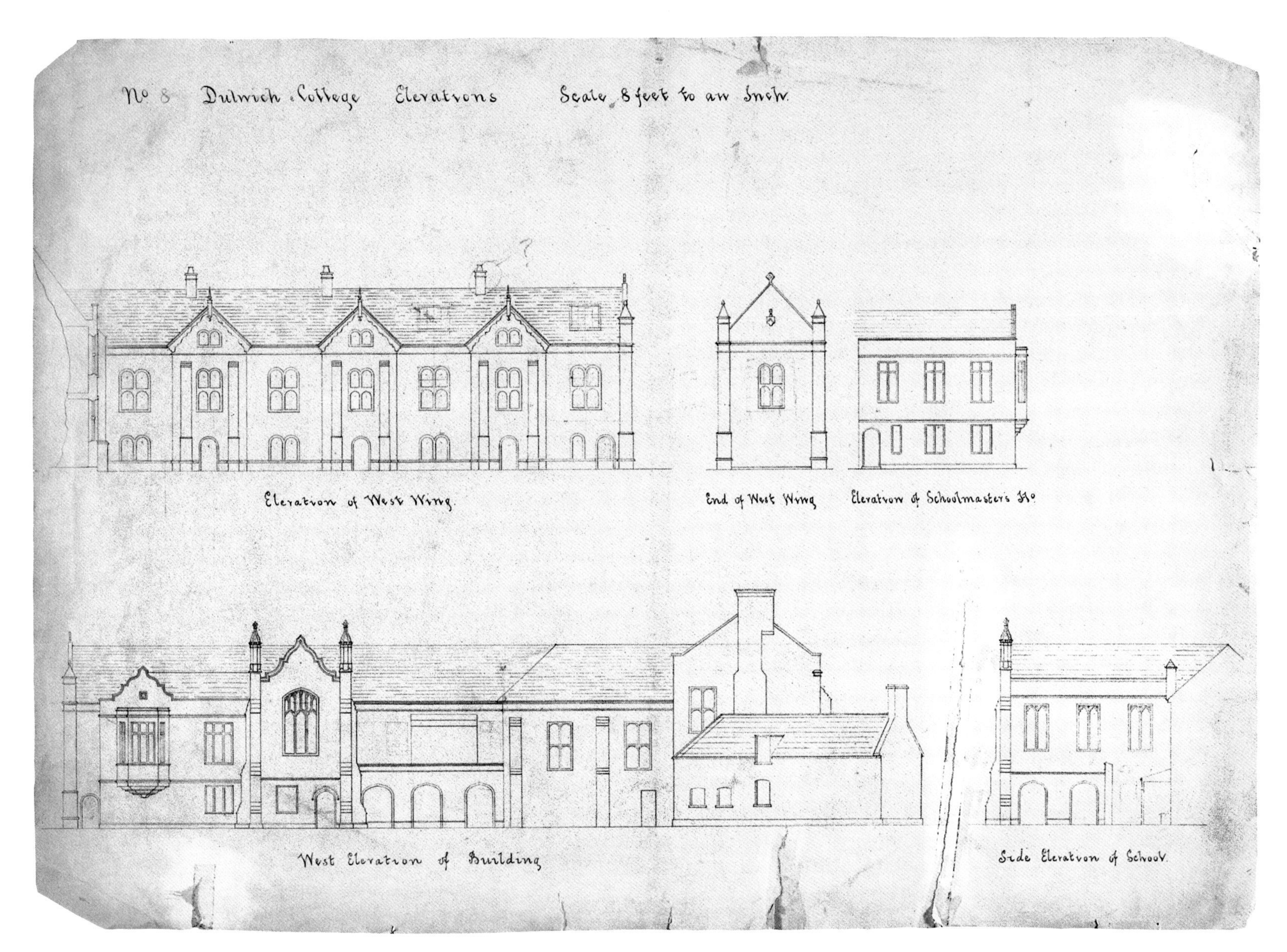

133
Elevations of the remodelled West Wing of the College
Charles Barry Junior 1858

Charles Barry Junior at Dulwich College: 1858 to 1900

Charles Barry Junior trained with his father and succeeded him as architect and surveyor to the Governors of Dulwich College Estate in 1858. His main contribution at Dulwich is the creation (from 1866 to 1870) of the new College further down College Road in a highly ornamented, Renaissance Revival style. He also radically altered the appearance of the quadrangle at the Old College. In some ways his most valuable contribution at the Old College is the complete set of survey plans and elevations illustrated here (Nos. 132–6, and No. 122), begun immediately after his appointment in 1858. Amongst other things this survey provides the best record of his father's work on the east wing of the College before he himself modified it.

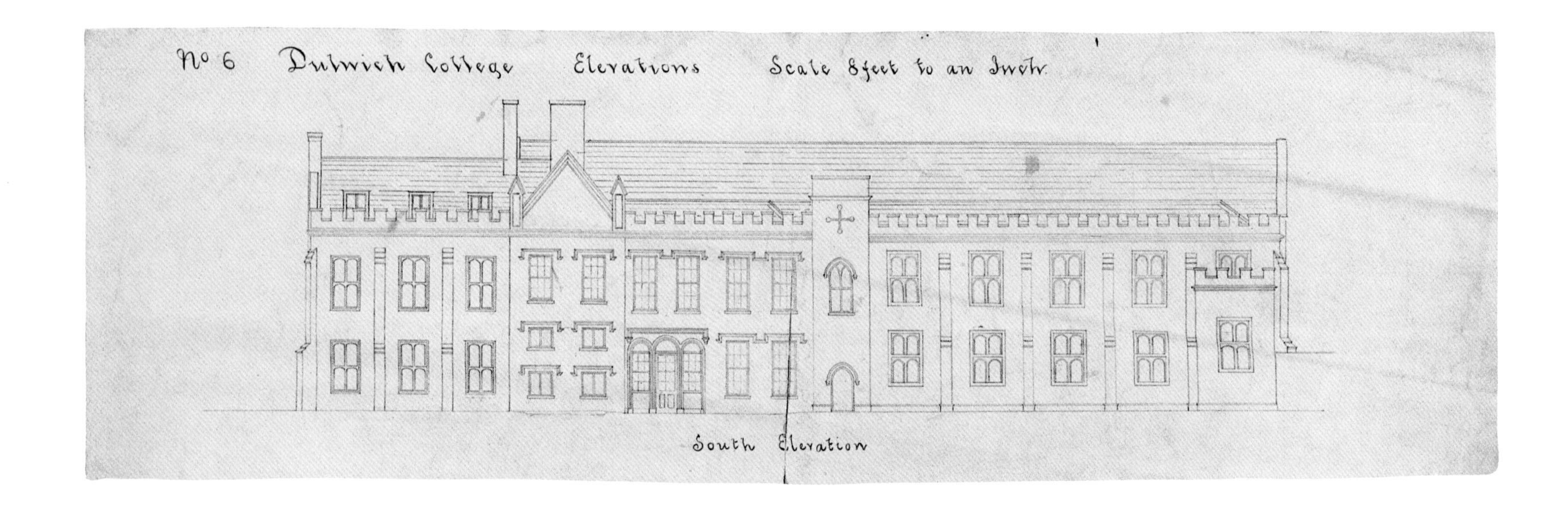

134
Elevation of the South Range
Charles Barry Junior 1858

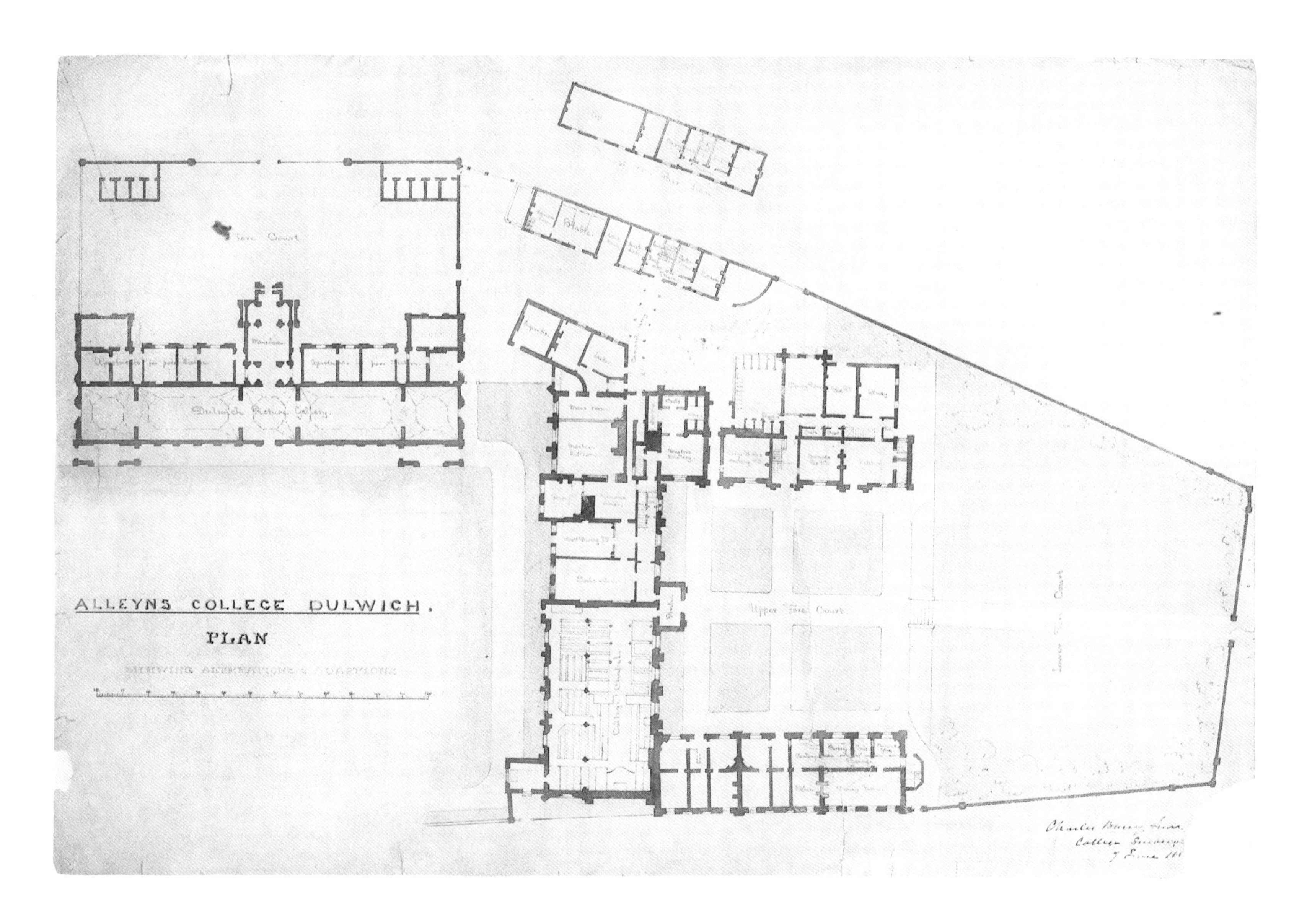

135

Ground Floor Plan to the College showing Alterations

Charles Barry Junior *c.* 1858

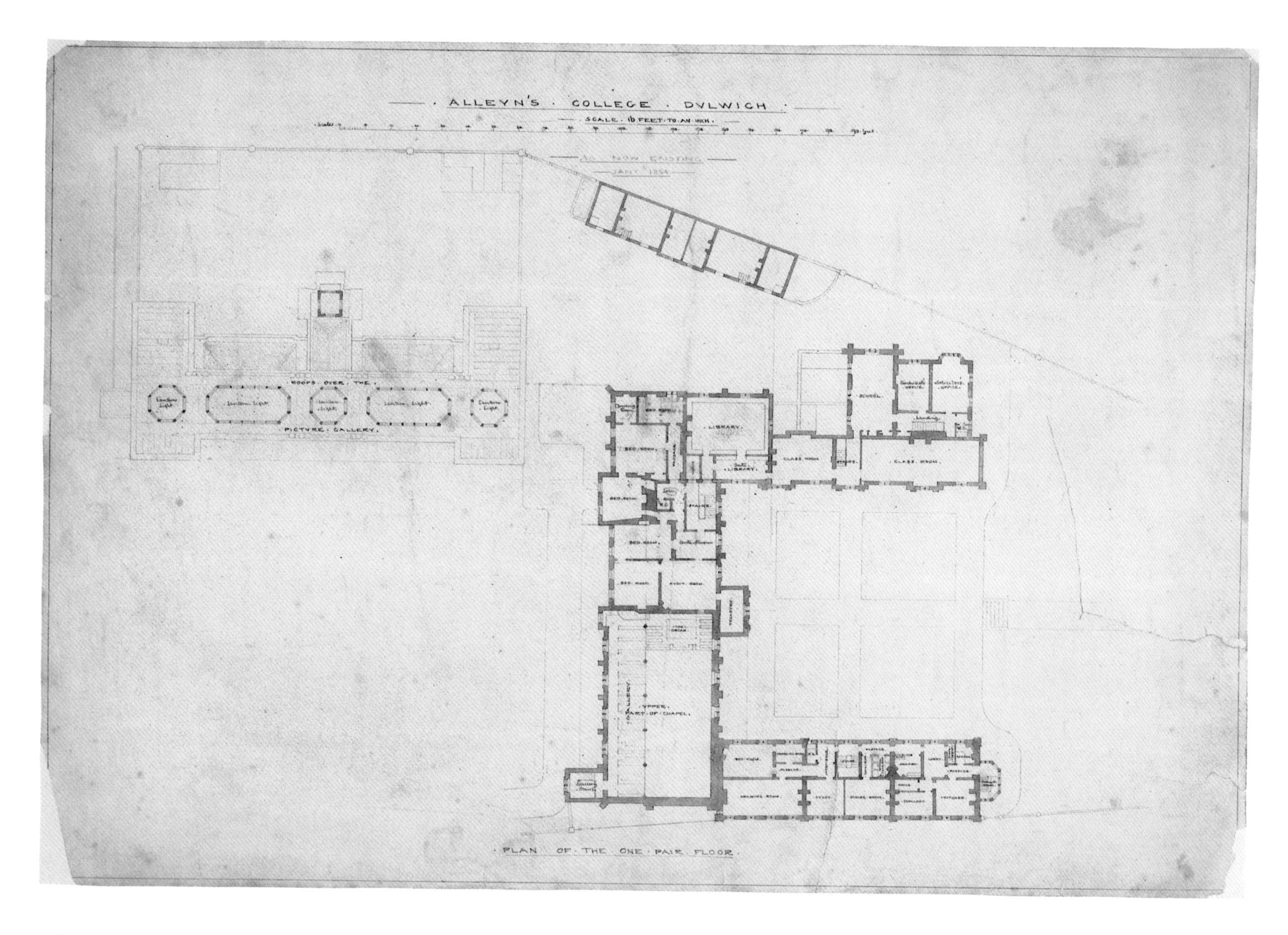

136

Upper Floor Plan to the College

Charles Barry Junior January 1864

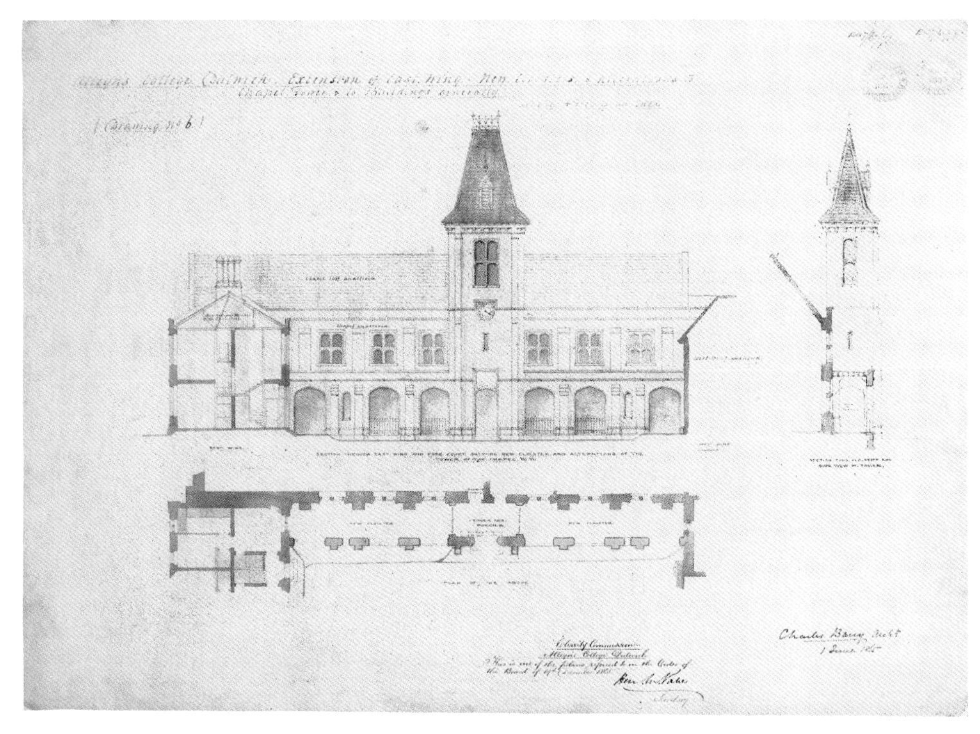

138
Elevation of the North Façade of the South Range of the College: showing the Proposed New Cloister and Alterations to Chapel Tower
Charles Barry Junior 1865

137
Neo-Elizabethan Design Proposal for the North Tower of the Chapel
Charles Barry Junior *c.* 1865

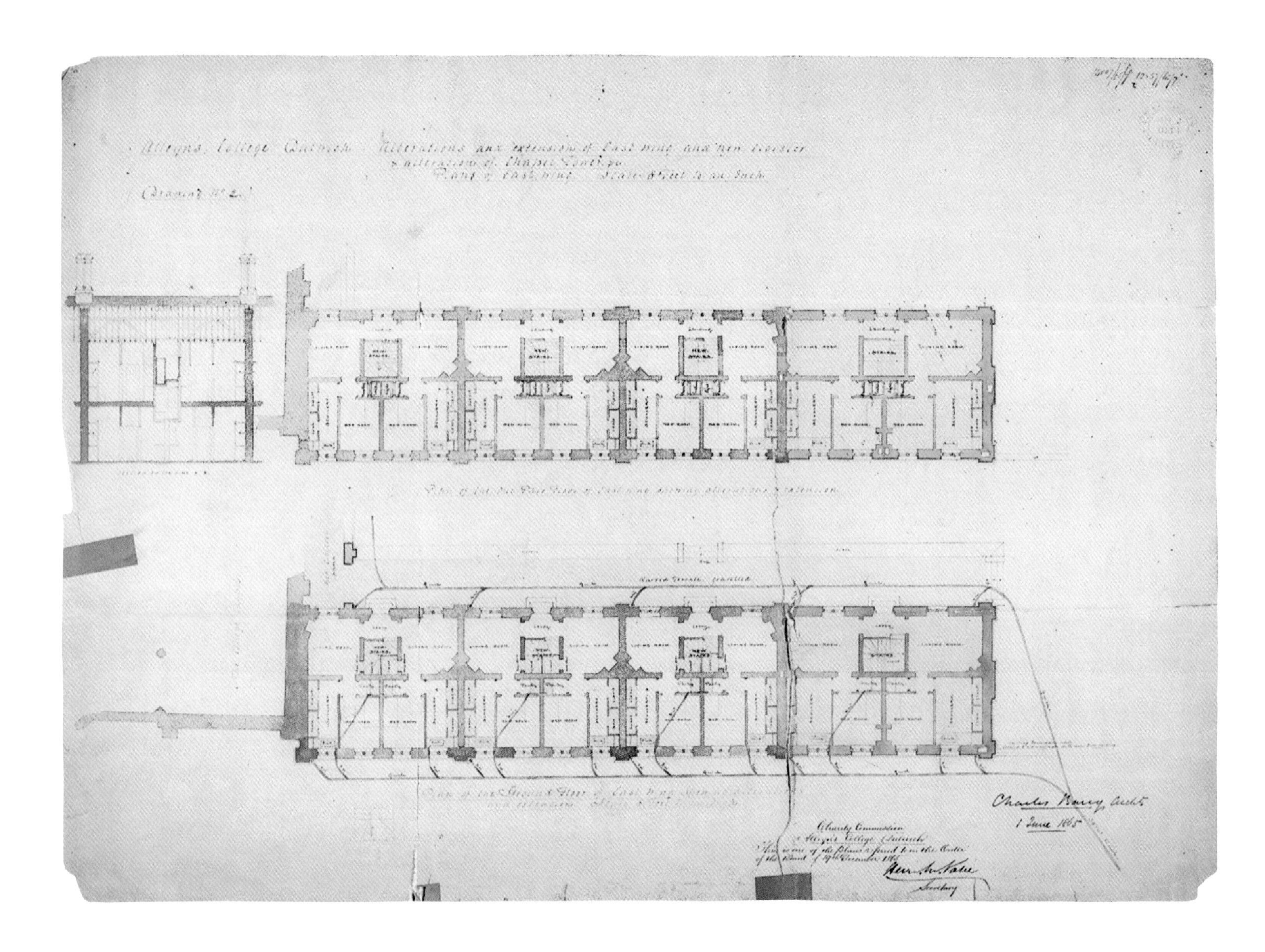

139

Plan and Section of the First and Ground Floors of the East Wing: showing Proposed Alterations

Charles Barry Junior 1 June 1865

141
Dulwich College From The North
Raphael Tuck & Sons c. 1913

140
South Façade of the College
c. 1890

The Victorian Gallery

In 1857 the Dulwich College constitution was reformed and a separate Picture Gallery Committee set up in place of the old Governing Body of Master, Warden, and four Fellows. At the first meeting of the new Picture Gallery Committee on 2 February 1858, Richard Redgrave RA (1804–88), the Surveyor of the Queen's Pictures, was invited to make a report on the 'present state of the Gallery of Paintings'. Redgrave's report of 26 March recommended a thorough Victorianisation of the interiors of the Gallery. The niches in Soane's vault should be replaced; 'the curve of the coving being made continuous'; Soane's 'monotonous' wall colour should have a 'varied treatment'; a new floor 'of coloured tiles' laid; the top sections of the sky lights glazed to admit more light; the ventilation improved; gas light installed; and a dado introduced 'with a projection of such height that the first range of pictures may rest upon it, and the hanging thus be continuous'.

Luckily Soane's vault was left alone as was the oak board floor laid some time between 1823 and 1846. The skylights were not altered until the Edwardian period and artificial light was not installed until 1977. However the original steam heaters were replaced during the nineteenth century with grilles (presumably for under-floor heating) and a dado was added as Redgrave advocated. Also at this time a continuous railing was set up round the Gallery.

Also in 1858 the Committee agreed to open the Gallery to the public for six days a week, without requiring visitors to buy tickets in advance. By the 1860s the large number of visitors to the Gallery began to feel a 'want of convenient arrangement', or what would now be called 'visitor facilities'. On 6 May 1866 it was decided to replace Tappen's porch at the south end of the Gallery with a new entrance block, designed by Charles Barry Junior, with 'retiring rooms for ladies and gentlemen' . This opened to the public on 1 May 1867.

In 1870 Dulwich College moved into their new premises, thus freeing up space within the Old College. This allowed the six old ladies to move out of the Gallery building and back into the Old College next door, which they did between 1872 and 1884. The almshouses thus became available for the Gallery's use. By 1884 Charles Barry Junior had converted the two end blocks into display space, creating the present Rooms VI and IX where his skylights can still be admired. The single-storey almshouses were converted into offices and stores, as can be seen by comparing the plans of 1858 and 1908 (Nos. 135 and 149).

142
Interior View of the Gallery
Rock & Co 1849

143
Interior View of Galleries I–V
c. 1880

144
Interior View of the Gallery
Joseph Dakin 1894

145
Interior of Gallery VI or IX
Emery Walker c. 1900

146
The Gallery from the South-West
c. 1900

147
The West Façade of the Gallery
c. 1900

148
The Gallery and College Buildings from the South
c. 1900

Extending the Picture Gallery: 1908 to 1938

The appointment in February 1908 of Henry Yates Thompson (1838–1928) as Chairman of the Gallery Committee marked a new period of expansion for the Gallery. Between 1908 and 1915 Yates Thompson had one of the single-storey almshouse blocks converted into display space (the present Room VIII) and four new rooms added along the east front of the Gallery (the present Rooms X to XII and the Entrance Hall), all to designs by E S Hall (1881–1940). Work stopped in 1915 however, before the fifth and final room on the east façade was added, which must have made it look very lopsided. In 1936 the Gallery's financial situation improved and it was decided to commission the architect H S Goodhart-Rendel (1887–1959) to fill this gap. In November 1936 he submitted plans for this north-east corner room (the present Room XIII) and for an enlarged entrance block at the south end of the Gallery. The estimate for these works came to £8,760 excluding architect's fees; the available funds were not sufficient and the decision was made 'to proceed with the erection of a copy of the South Gallery of the existing building' (that is Room XIII). This addition only cost £2,000 and in January 1938 the work was completed.

150

Gallery Interior: Room IX called 'The Gem Room'

c. 1910

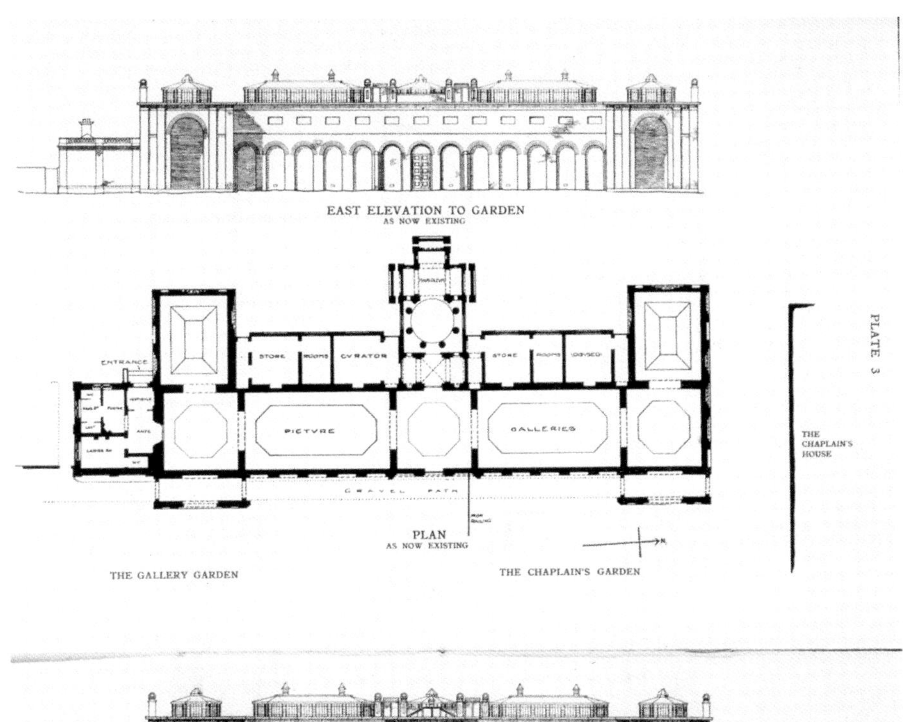

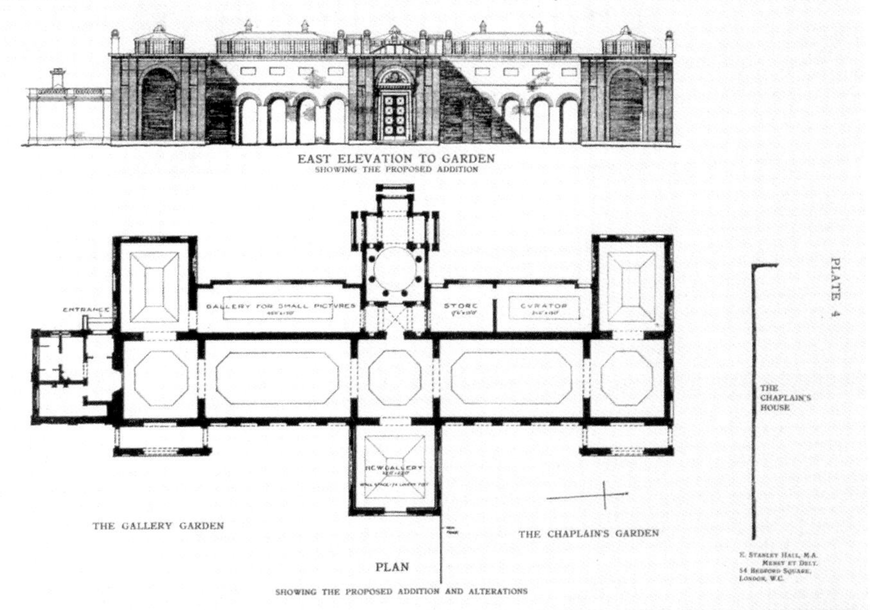

149

Plan and East Elevation of the Gallery: Existing and Proposed

E S Hall 1908

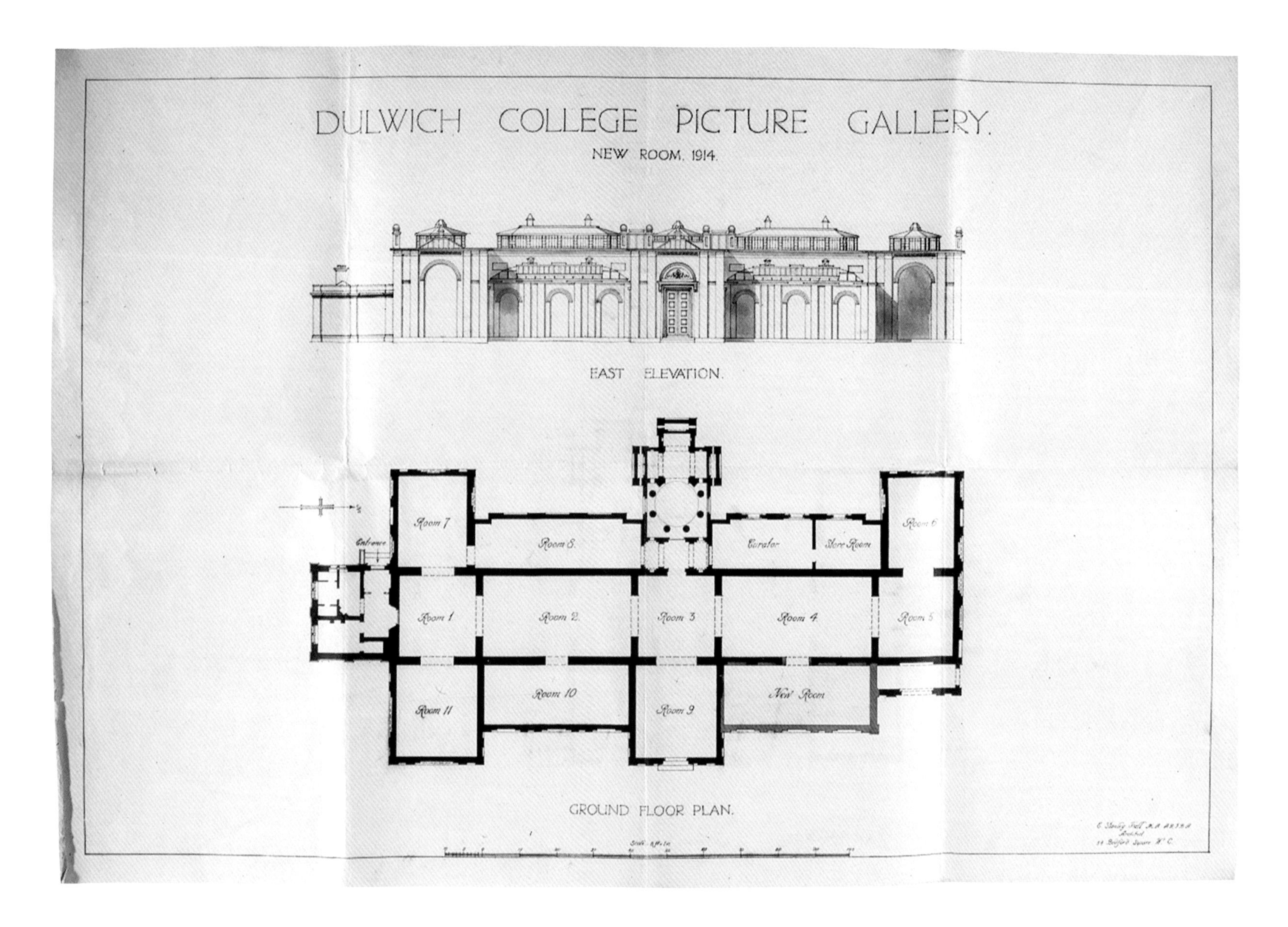

151
Plan and East Elevation of the Gallery
E S Hall 1914

152
View of the North – East Screen 1920 – 35

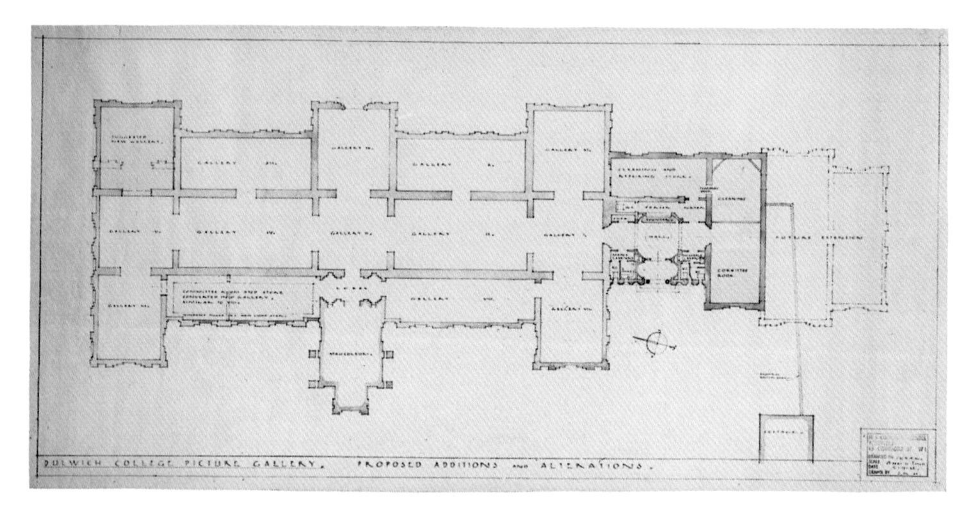

153

Plan of the Gallery showing Proposed Alterations and Extension

JKH for *HS Goodhart-Rendel Architect*

5 November 1936

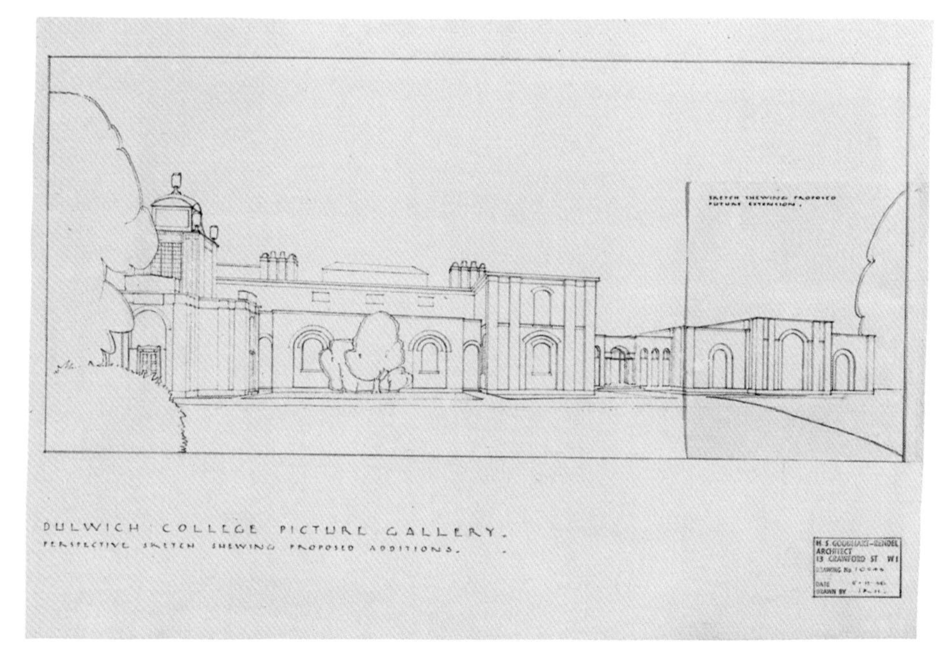

154

Perspective Sketch of the West Façade with the Proposed Extension at the South End of the Gallery

JKH for *HS Goodhart-Rendel Architect*

5 November 1936

155
Elevation of Proposed Extension at the South End of the Gallery
HCL for *Goodhart-Rendel Architect* 5 November 1936

156 East Façade of the Gallery 1938

157 **West Façade of the Gallery** 1938

War Damage: 1944

On 12 July 1944, a V1 flying bomb ('Doodlebug') landed in Gallery Road between the College and the Gallery. The resulting damage is recorded in the following photographs, taken in the immediate aftermath. Fortunately the paintings had been removed earlier to a Welsh slate mine.

159
Bomb Damage: College and the Gallery West Façade
1944

158
Bomb Damage: South-West Corner of the College and the Gallery
1944

160

Bomb Damage: South Façade of the College

1944

161

Bomb Damage: Gallery West Façade

1944

163

Bomb Damage: Gallery Interior, Rooms I–V

1944

162
Bomb Damage: View through Gallery VI
1944

The Old College and the Gallery Rebuilt: 1945 to 1998

Soane's architecture was far more revered in 1945 than it had been in the nineteenth century and the decision to rebuild his Gallery was made quickly. In December 1945, Sir John Summerson, then the Curator of Sir John Soane's Museum, wrote in the Architect's Journal: 'The decision to rebuild Dulwich will be endorsed by anyone who has the slightest respect for architecture as a fine art'. The architects of the Dulwich Estate, Austin Vernon and Partners, were employed to undertake the work, with Arthur Davis, RA, and Sir Edward Maufe, RA, acting as consultants. The total cost of rebuilding amounted to £60,000, of which £20,000 was provided by the Pilgrim Trust and £30,000 by the War Damage Commission. Funds for modernisation were not available, however, and electricity was not introduced into the Gallery until 1977.

The Gallery was formally re-opened by the Queen Mother on 27 April 1953. Sir John Summerson wrote in *The Times* on 1 May 1953 that it had been 'reconstructed loyally and with excellent appreciation of Soane's original', concluding that 'the Dulwich Gallery embodies Soane's eccentric, haunting genius as no other surviving work of his (except his own museum); and many visitors to Dulwich will find themselves as much moved by its resurrection as by the freshened beauties of Poussin and Watteau.'

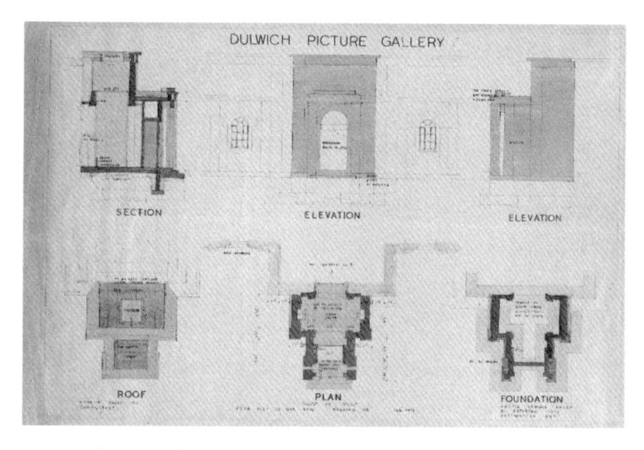

165 Plan, Elevation and Section of the Porch on the East Façade *Austin Vernon* February 1951

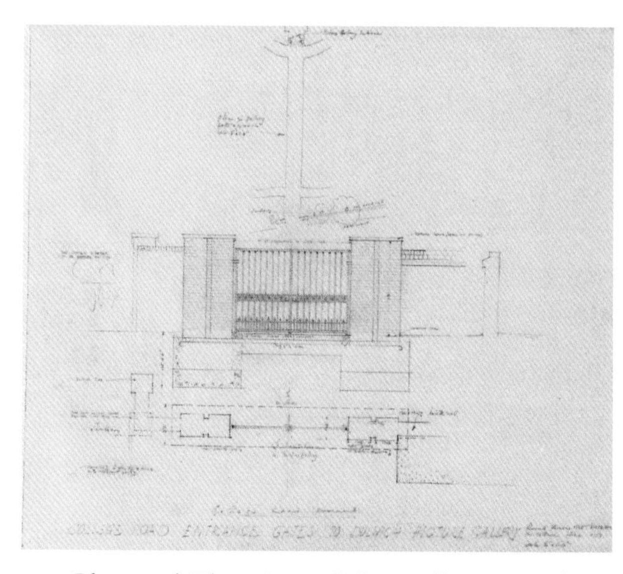

166 Plan and Elevation of the College Road Entrance Gates to the Gallery *Russell Vernon* 1951

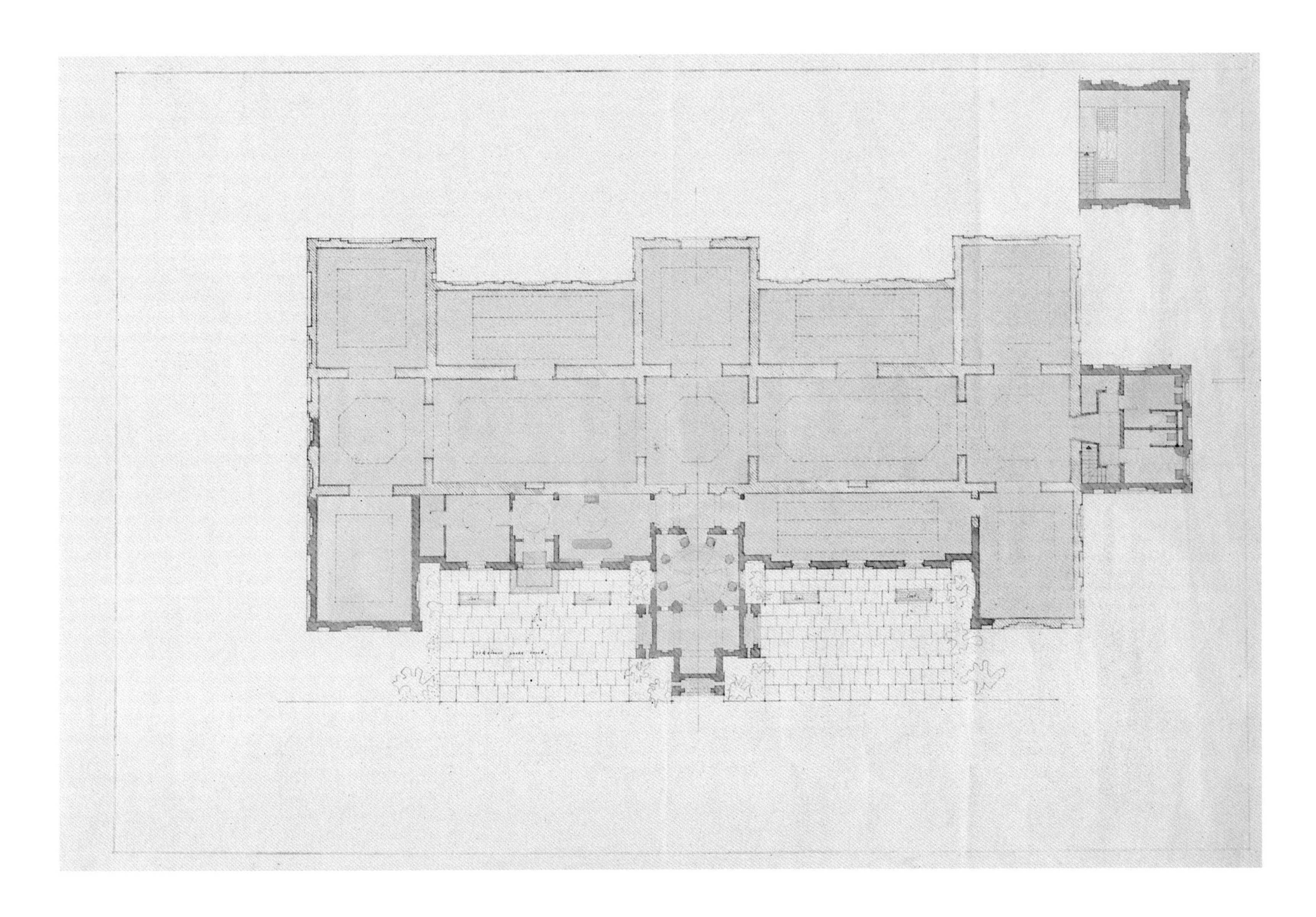

164
Plan of the Gallery Showing Post-War Rebuilding and Proposed Alterations
Austin Vernon 1948

167
The South Façade of the Gallery
Martin Charles 1981

168 The East Façade of the Gallery *Martin Charles* 1981

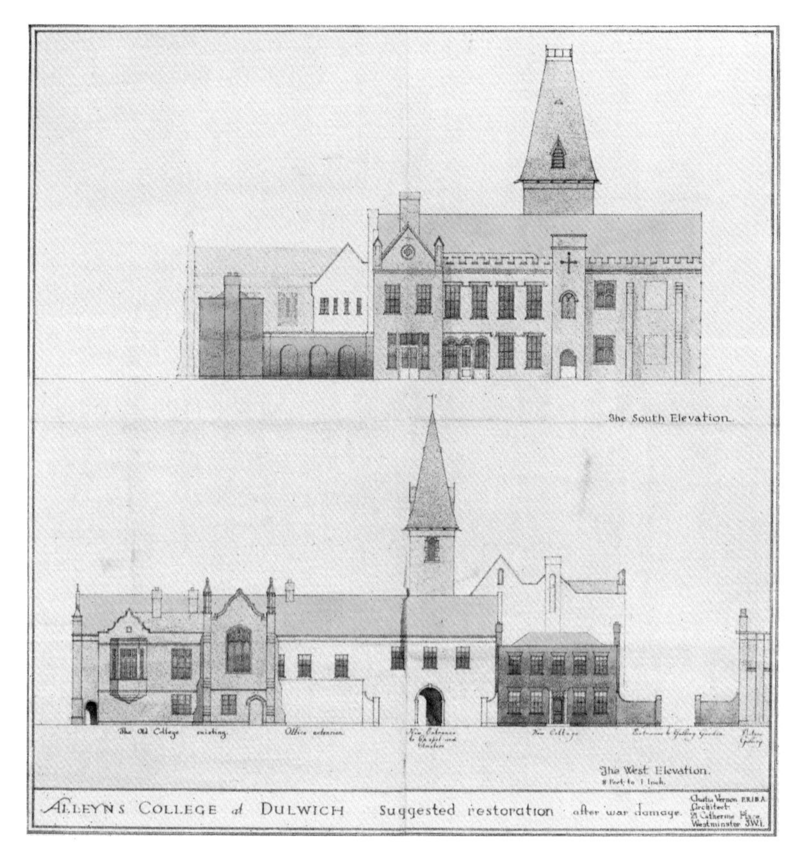

169

South and West Elevations of the Old College

Austin Vernon c. 1948

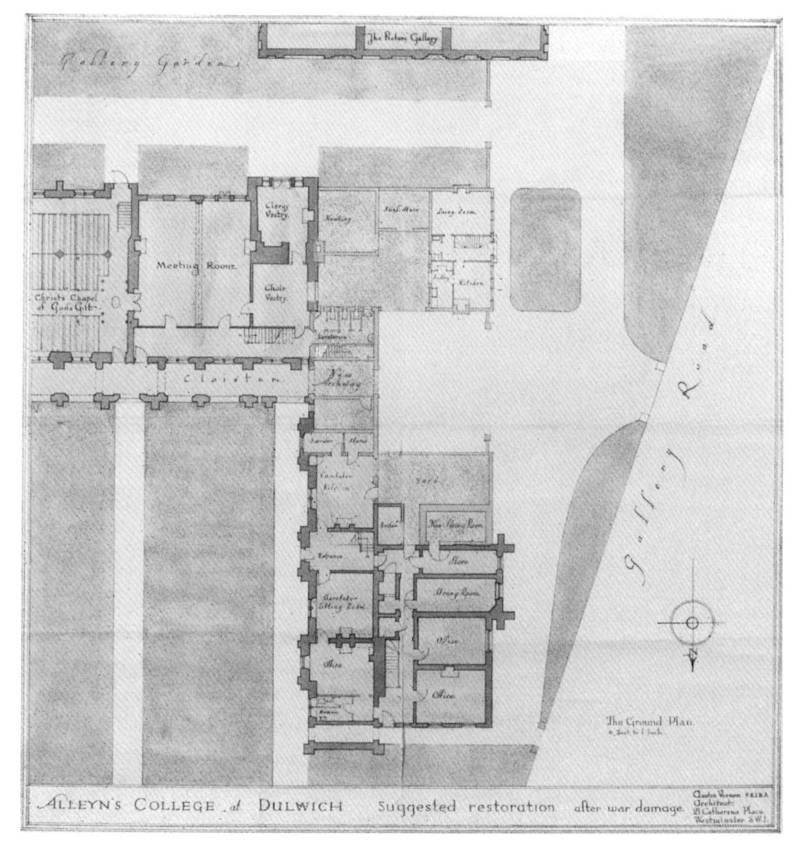

170

Ground Plan of Half the South Range and the West Wing of the College

Austin Vernon c. 1948

172

Plan and Elevation of the West Façade of the College

Austin Vernon September 1953

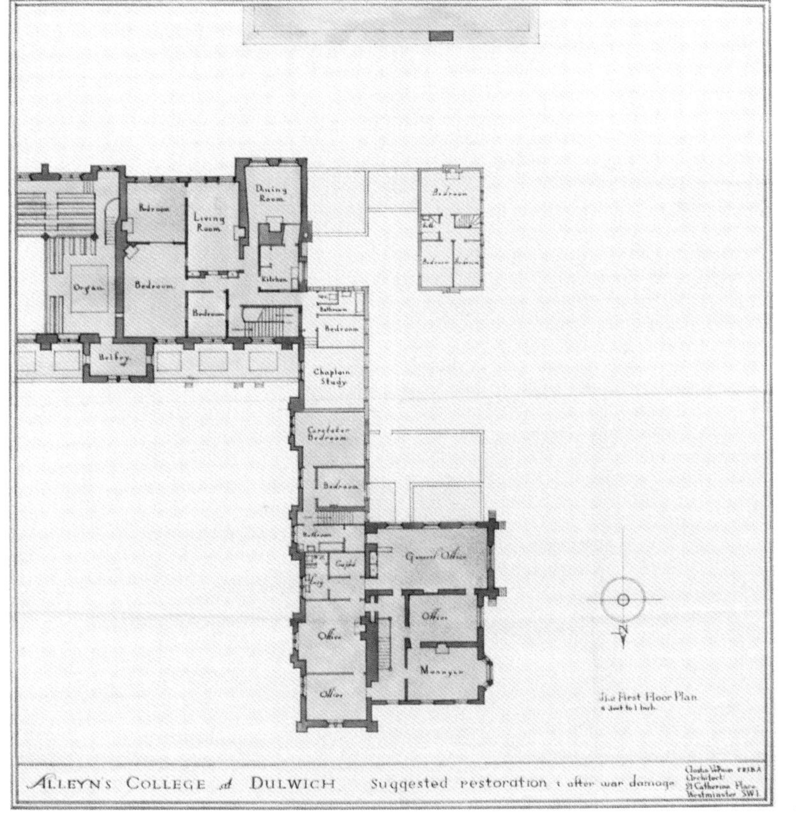

171

First Floor Plan of Half the South Range and the West Wing of the College

Austin Vernon *c.* 1948

173 **Dulwich College from the North** *John Hammond* April 2000

174
The Gallery and South Façade of the South Range of the Old College and Chapel
Martin Charles 1981

175 **Galleries I–V** *c.* 1960

176
Galleries I–V
Martin Charles 1981

177
The Mausoleum
Martin Charles 1981

179
The Interior of the Mausoleum showing Soane's *'lumière mystérieuse'*
Martin Charles 1981

178
The Interior of the Mausoleum
Martin Charles 1981

180
Interior Room IX
Martin Charles 1981

181
Interior Room XII
Martin Charles 1981

Rick Mather Architects: Refurbishment and New Building: December 1995 to May 2000

In 1994 the governance of the Gallery passed from the College to an independent board of Trustees, under the Chairmanship of Lord Sainsbury of Preston Candover, KG. In 1995 it was decided to embark upon a major refurbishment and rebuilding programme taking advantage of the recently established Heritage Lottery Fund. In December 1995 Rick Mather was appointed as architect. In May 2000 the work was completed at a cost of £8.5 million, raised from the Heritage Lottery Fund and many individual donors.

Included here is a small group of Rick Mather's designs, executed by members of his office. The Project Architect was Matthew McGrory. The simultaneous completion of the building and this book means that only one actual photograph could be included.

The project can be divided into two parts: the refurbishment of the Soane building and the creation of a new pavilion along College Road. Much of the work within the Soane building concerns the introduction of new technology – air-conditioning, daylight control and artificial lighting. However there are many elements of architectural restoration which relate to the history of the building as set out in this book. The east façade has been restored to something of its original Soanean appearance; Goodhart-Rendel's Room XIII has been re-created by clearing out the store and lavatories put there after the war; the door cut into Room V in 1945–52 has been blocked off; the Barry skylight has been restored to Room VI; Room VII has been given a skylight to match that of Room VIII, designed by ES Hall; the vaults in Rooms XI and XII have been lowered to allow a better view of Soane's attic; the cork tiled floor has been replaced by wide-board oak; the original colours of the enfilade have been excavated and recreated. All these improvements to restore the appearance of the Gallery soon after it opened to the public for the first time in 1814.

The new building has been sited along College Road following the line of the garden wall, first seen in No. 2, and recalling its presence by matching its brick-work. The West side of the new building, the chapel and the Soane building mark three sides of a rectangular 'second quadrangle' in a response to Soane's original intentions to create a collegiate quadrangle, seen, for example, in Nos. 16 and 24. Rick Mather's quadrangle is surrounded by a bronze and glass cloister linking all the parts of the new and old buildings. The spacing and dimensions of the bronze 'fins' supporting the sun-shade of the cloister and their pilaster-like character are directly derived from the buttresses of the Chapel. The story of the architecture of the College and Gallery therefore comes full circle with a form – the buttress – which has occurred in so many different guises and which has exerted so powerful an influence.

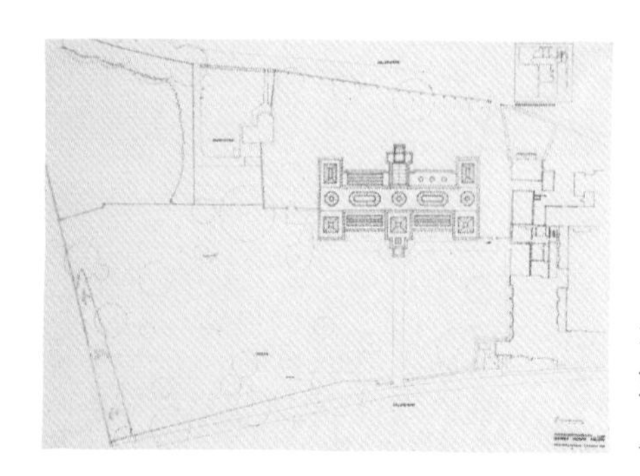

182

First Floor Survey Plan

Rick Mather Architects 1996

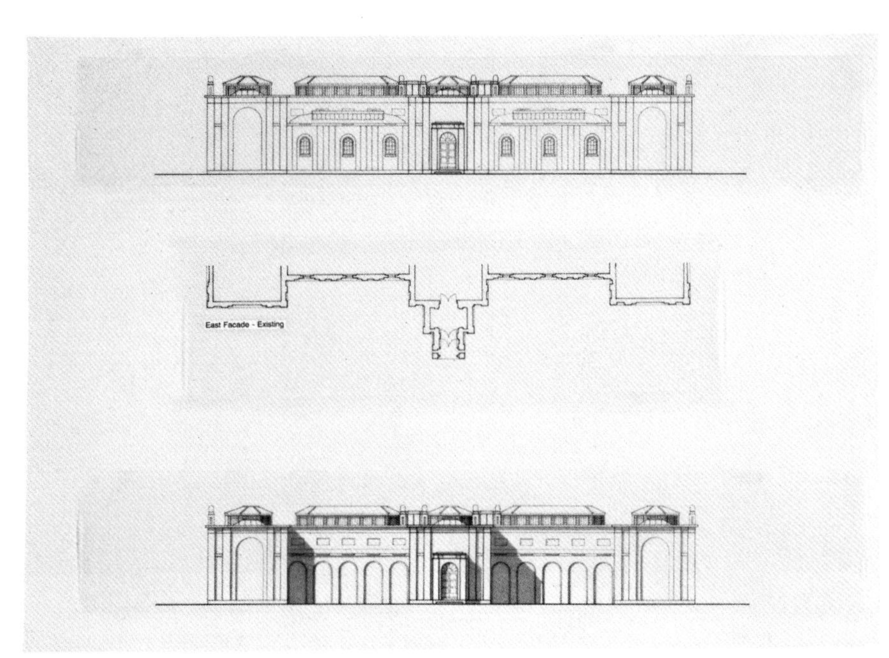

183a

East Façade – Existing

Rick Mather Architects 16 October 1996

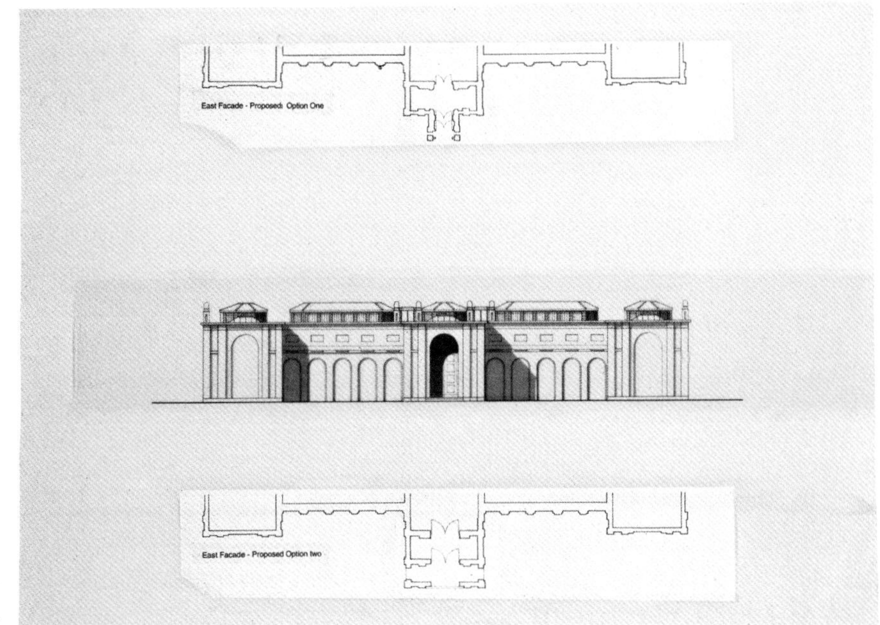

183b

East Façade – Proposed Options One and Two

Rick Mather Architects 16 October 1996

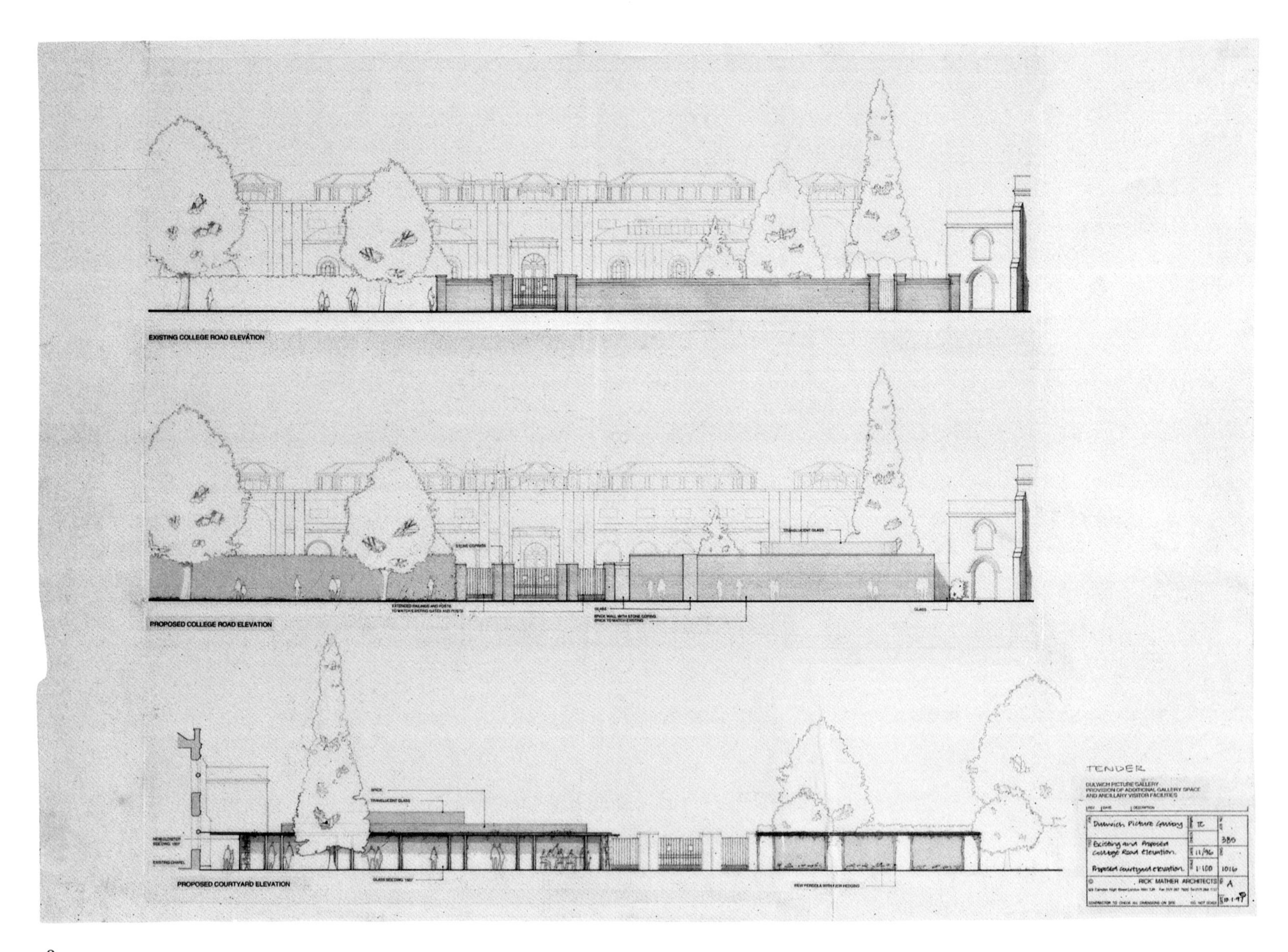

184

Existing and Proposed College Road Elevation

Tim Carter for *Rick Mather Architects* 10 January 1997

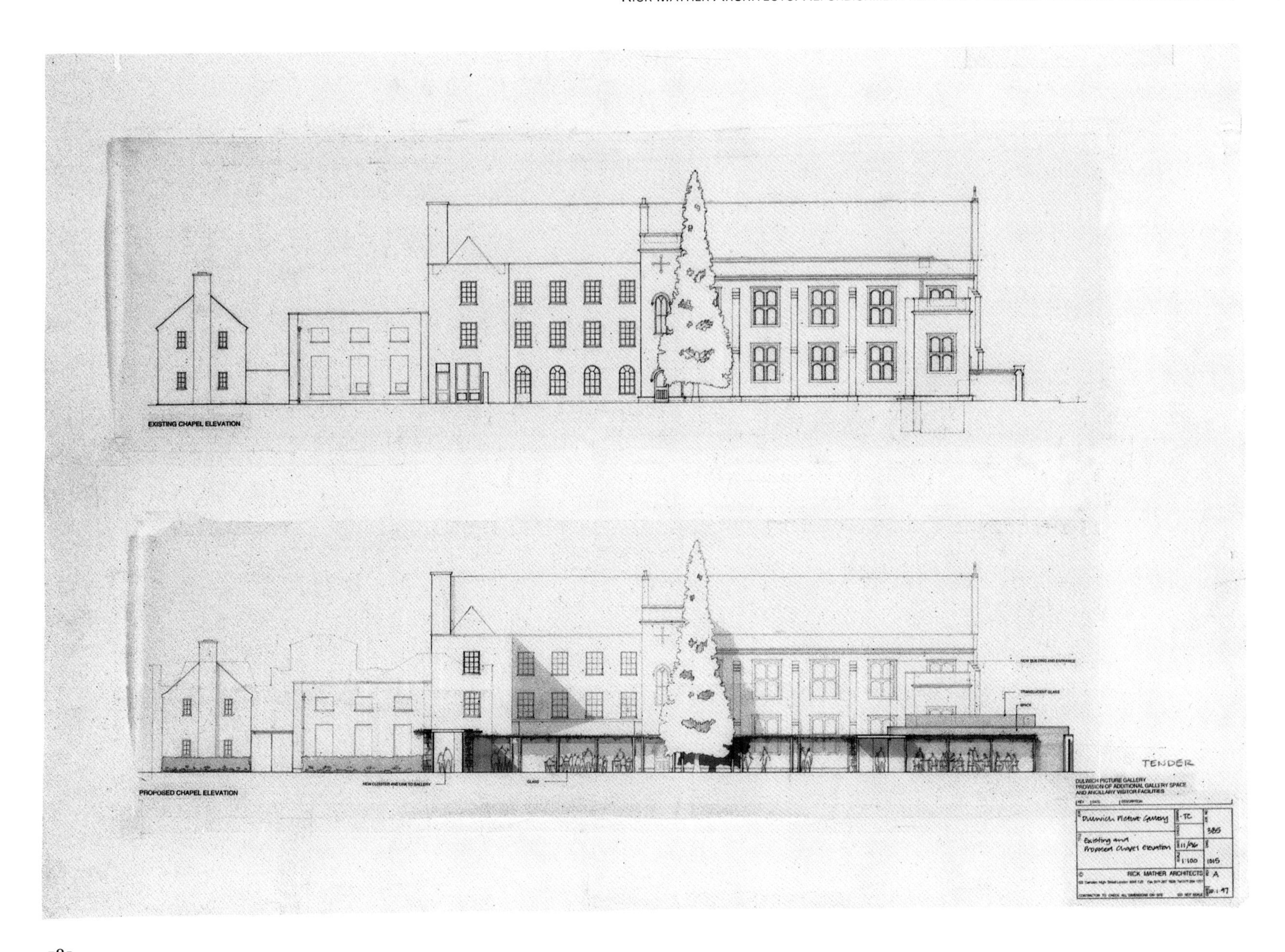

185

Existing and Proposed Chapel Elevation

Tim Carter for *Rick Mather Architects* 10 January 1997

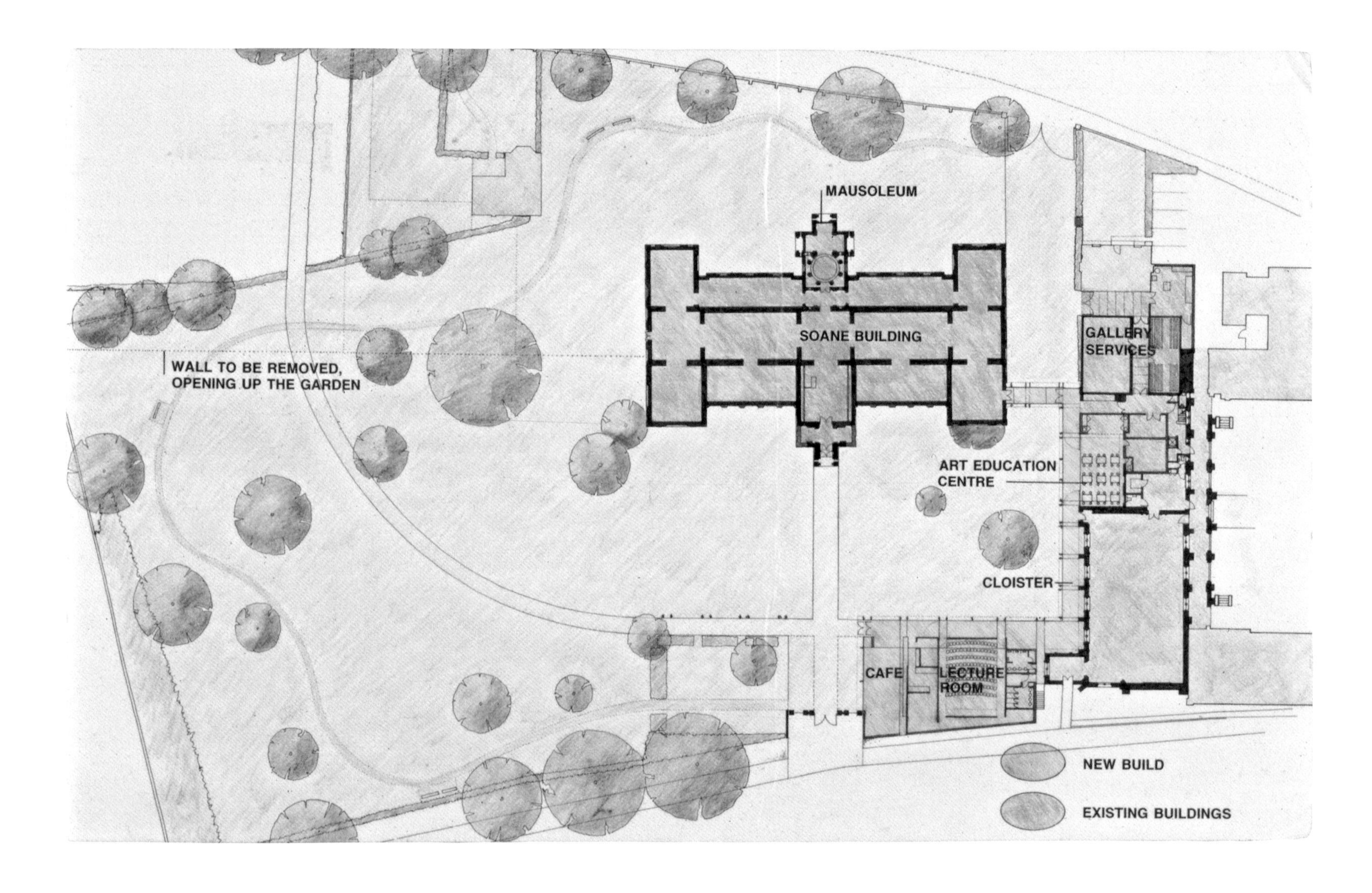

186

Proposed Ground Plan

Rick Mather Architects 1996

187
Gallery Interior
Rooms I–V
John Hammond May 2000

Dulwich College 1613 to 1811

1

Map of London

Jean Rocque

1748, engraving, 69 × 80 cm

Dulwich College

Located due south of the City of London, in the mid eighteenth century Dulwich Village was set in open country side, 'secluded', as a visiting surveyor described it in 1808, 'from the bustle and activity of trade and commerce'.

2

Dulwich College

J Oliphant

1785, engraving, 22.2 × 33.1 cm

Inscr. 'Dulwich College/Drawn and engraved for Harrison's History of London, & c'; 'J Oliphant delin.'; [In pencil] '1785'.

Dulwich College

The College chapel, seen here from the south-east in its rural setting, probably appears as it did in Edward Alleyn's time. Note the bare tower, the four buttresses and the simple chancel window at its east end. All these elements were altered in the nineteenth century: the tower was re-clad; the chapel was widened; and the chancel window was remodelled in a more ornate style by the architect Charles Barry Junior (see No. 132). There is no record of the original east wing of Alleyn's College; the simple Georgian block we see here, with its giant Doric pilasters, owes its appearance to a remodelling of 1728–9.

3

Dulwich College

T Cadel

1792, etching, 15 × 16 cm

Inscr. 'Dulwich College. Pl. 2/Published as the Act directs, March 1st 1792 by T Cadel, Strand.'

Dulwich College

This shows the south side of the College as Soane would have known it, with the chapel to the right of the tower and the Master's lodgings to its left. We see here the Jacobean cross windows of the chapel, with their four arched lights, which were a significant influence on Soane's designs for the Gallery.

4

Dulwich College

Taylor

1796, engraving, 12 × 21.1 cm

Inscr. 'European Magazine/View of Dulwich College/Published by I Sewell, 1796. Taylor Sculp'

Dulwich College

This print records the same stage in the evolution of the College as the previous views, but seen from the main quadrangle to the north. Soane's eye must have been caught by the central (southern) range, housing the chapel and Master's lodgings. In place of the buttresses seen on the rear façade of the chapel (see previous views) the architect has here used giant Doric piers with a section of entablature broken forward over them upon which rests a stone ball. One of these massive stone balls still survives in the garden of Gallery Cottage. If this façade dates from 1619 (as is usually assumed) then it is a very advanced design indeed and must have seemed to Soane worthy of Inigo Jones (1573–1652) – a signatory on the 1619 document for the incorporation of Alleyn's College. Almost all Soane's own designs for Dulwich employ some version of this Doric buttress-pier form.

The right (west) wing seen in this print, which housed the original gallery, was remodelled in 1661 – the date occurs on an inscription recorded in a Soane survey drawing (No. 7, SM 65/4/01). On the north side, the quadrangle is closed off by a wall, pierced centrally by a decorative wrought-iron gate made by George Bunker. When this wall was demolished in 1819 the bricks were recycled in order to build the entrance lodge at the south end of the Gallery (see Private Sittings books in the College Archive for 10 May 1819).

5

Map of Dulwich (Detail)

1806, black and coloured ink

30 × 30 cm

Inscr. 'A Plan of the Manor/Dulwich/in the County of Surrey/1806'

Dulwich College

This map of 1806, which only recently has come to light, is the most informative plan of the College and its site before the building of Soane's Gallery. To the south-west of the College and almost on the site of the current Gallery, there stood a long, rectangular structure, which may be identified as 'the old stables in front of the picture gallery' referred to in the 'Private Sittings' book of the College on 24 July 1814, when the College architect, George Tappen, was commissioned to build new stables along Gallery Road. This earlier structure can also be seen in a building progress view of the Gallery (No. 107, SM Vol 81/18). On the site of the present Gallery gardens, there was a windmill and, further to the south, two old houses, for which a demolition order was issued on 16 February 1815. On the east-west axis directly in front of the Gallery was the 'mill pond', which still appears, though in a reduced form, in a mid nineteenth-century view (No. 128).

The Commissioning of Sir John Soane

6

West Wing of the College: Plan and Section of the First Floor housing the Picture Gallery

GA Underwood

28 February 1811, pencil, 34.3 × 58.5 cm

Inscr. 'Dulwich College/Feb. 28 1811'

SM 65/4/04

This is the first dated drawing from Soane's Office for work at Dulwich. It is a survey drawing – annotated with a scale and measurements – of the existing gallery on the upper floor of the west wing. It was executed by George Allen Underwood (*c.* 1793–1829), then aged 18 and an articled pupil in Soane's Office from 1807 to 1815.

7

West Wing of the College: East Elevation

Soane Office

Early 1811?, pencil, 23.9 x39.6 cm

Inscr. 'West Front [sic]/1661 [on the building]'

SM 65/4/01

The College authorities were aware of the need to refurbish this wing, which is dated 1661 in the inscription on this drawing. Soane, having had made an accurate survey of the College, declared it to be in a 'ruinous state'.

8

West Wing of the College: East Elevation

Soane Office

Early 1811?, pencil, 33 × 57 cm

Inscr. 'East Side of West Wing'

SM 65/4/03

The giant Doric pilaster order, which Soane later reinterpreted on the Gallery building, is clearly visible in this survey elevation (though not in the earlier view, No. 4). Here the order decorates the three projecting bays, enclosing Jacobean windows similar to those of the chapel.

9

Ground Plan of the College, with sections of the East and West Wings

GA Underwood

5 June 1811, pencil and brown ink with grey and pink wash, 34 × 58 cm

Inscr. 'Dulwich College/June 5th 1811/The Establishment Constitutes/of A Master – Mr Allen 4 Rooms/Warden – Mr Allen 3 Rooms/Minister – Mr Smith 4 Rooms 1 Cellar/School Master – Mr Julian – 4 Rooms 1 Cellar/An Usher – Mr Corry 3 Rooms 1 Cellar/Organist – Mr Dowell 1 Room 1 Cellar/No. 6 Old Women 6 Rooms/ 6 Old Men 12 Rooms/12 Boys 2 Rooms/ Butler 2 Rooms/Cook 2 Rooms/Scullery Maid 1 Room/House Maid 3 Rooms.'

SM 65/4/02

This scaled plan, also attributable to Underwood, shows the arrangement of the entire College complex, with the uses of the rooms marked up. The west wing housed the alms women; the east wing the alms men and scholars; and the south wing the chapel and lodging for the Warden and Master. Projecting to the south of this south range are two further structures, marked in pencil. Part of the single-story building, lying furthest to the south-west, survived until 1944 (its rubble is visible in No. 158). The building just in front of the site where the Gallery now stands may be 'the old stable in front of the picture gallery' visible on the 1806 map (see No. 5).

This survey was carried out some way into the design process (soon after No. 32, SM 65/4/41). In one respect it is more than a mere record of the site: comparison with Nos. 2 and 3 shows that the buttresses of the chapel have been widened into piers and the infilling building cleared out. In pencil a line marks the west end of the south range, were it exactly twice the length of the chapel (compare No. 14 ff.) – this provides the scale for Soane's proposed new quadrangle designs.

10

Plan of the Chapel

Soane Office

Early 1811?, pencil and grey wash, 33 × 56 cm

Inscr: 'Chapel/Line of Gallery'

SM 65/4/05

This detailed survey drawing shows the buttresses on the south side of the chapel more accurately than the previous drawing, but the low building seen in No.3 in its south-east bay is omitted – this is the site where Soane initially proposed building the mausoleum according to Bourgeois will (see Nos. 15 and 16, SM 65/4/06 and 07). On this plan Soane also records two recesses on the exterior of the east end of the chapel, these may represent the plan of the low roofed structure seen under the chancel window in No.2.

Soane's 'Designs One to Five': April to May 1811

11

Design for the New Gallery: Front and Rear Elevation

Soane Office

April 1811?, pencil and grey wash,

32 × 53.5 cm

SM 65/4/29

This undated sheet shows the front and back elevation of a new Gallery building and would appear to be a preparatory study for the earliest dated design (No. 12, SM 65/4/28), on the same size and type of paper. In this drawing Soane marks in a skylight; even at this early stage he is thinking about the top lighting for which the Gallery is famous. The lower windows shown here would presumably have been blind.

In both these elevations and in many of his subsequent designs, Soane used a simple incised pilaster to articulate the façades. The central bay is crowned by an attic containing a lunette window and surmounted by a shallow triangular pediment. The combination of the motifs lends a classicising character to these elevations, despite the use of Neo-Jacobean windows loosely copied from those of the College Chapel.

12

Design for the Entrance Façade of the Gallery

GA Underwood

4 April 1811, pencil and grey wash,

32 × 53.5 cm

Inscr. 'Dulwich College/April 4th 1811'

SM 65/4/28

This is the earliest securely dated design for the Gallery. It was executed by George Underwood, the only member of Soane's Office recorded as working on Dulwich on 4 April 1811. Underwood here develops the ideas of the previous sheet with the addition of a projecting porch. The end bays have been widened and are now framed by paired pilasters, while the attic storey and lunette window are still present, but in a reduced and altered form. The simple, block-like character of the porch and attic recalls the Neoclassicism of Soane's French contemporary, Claude-Nicholas Ledoux (1735–1806). This design anticipates No. 24 (SM 65/4/15), which would suggest that this façade was also planned to face onto College Road. The length of the Gallery here – 148 feet – is surprisingly close to the length as built – 154 feet.

13

Design for the Entrance Façade of the Gallery

Soane Office

April 1811?, pen and ink with blue, grey and brown wash, 17.1 × 42.5 cm

Inscr. 'Dulwich College'

V&A 3306.176

This finely coloured drawing is a slightly reduced copy of the previous monochrome design. Here Soane has added a wreath and garland motif in the pediment over the entrance, and further decorative elements in the frieze.

14

Dulwich College and Gallery: Design No. 1. Plan for a Quadrangle

G Bailey

17 April 1811, pencil, grey and white wash, 48.5 × 70 cm

Inscr. 'Dulwich College No. 1/LI Fields/ 17 April 1811/Chapel/Mausoleum/Tower/ Porch/Arcades/Stair Room/Rooms for the person app.ed to look after the pictures'

SM 65/4/43

This drawing is the first project plan for Soane's building work at Dulwich. It shows clearly the ambitious scale on which he wished to work. The east and west wings of the College are lightly indicated as due for demolition. Though the south wing is retained, its west half is completely remodelled in order to be a mirror image of the chapel which makes up its east half (compare with No. 9, SM 65/4/02). Soane repeated this south range for all his quadrangular designs; even the length of the block is consistently around 147 feet, double the length of the chapel and close to that of the Gallery. Soane lays out his new quadrangle to the south of this remodelled range: an almost identical block facing it about 137 feet to the south, with a stair well in the central projection to mirror the chapel tower, and a linking wing to the west. An open arcade is clearly marked, running around two and a half sides of this quadrangle. The mausoleum projects from the south-east corner of the chapel. It flanks the main College Road entrance, like a gatehouse, opposite an identical block marked 'rooms for the person app[rov]ed to look after the pictures'.

This drawing was executed by George Bailey (1792–1860), then aged 19. Bailey remained in Soane's office as an assistant until Soane's death, when by the architect's will he became the first curator of Sir John Soane's Museum. In Soane's hand, an initial proposal for his 'H' plan, Design No. 2 (see No. 18, SM 65/4/09) has been sketched over Bailey's finished drawing.

15

Dulwich College and Gallery: Design No. 1, Drawing No. 1. Plan

Soane Office

April 1811, pencil, brown ink, with grey and pink wash, 35.1 × 51.8 cm

Inscr. 'No. I/Dulwich College/Design No. 1/Chapel/Tower/Porch/Mausoleum/Gallery/ April 1811'

SM 65/4/06

Although lacking in some of its detail, this plan is close to the previous one. The College buildings that Soane proposed demolishing are again marked in pencil on the right of the plan. As in all of this group of designs, Soane envisaged retaining only the south range with the College chapel. The Gallery is here clearly marked in the long range placed opposite the chapel. This plan and the previous one still record the garden wall seen in No. 2.

16

Dulwich College and Gallery: Design No. 1, Drawing No. 2. Perspective View

G Bailey

17 April 1811, pencil and watercolour, 32.2 × 46.5 cm

Inscr. 'No. II/Dulwich College/Design No. 1/Lincolns Inn Fields/17 Ap. 1811'

SM 65/4/07

This perspective view, also called 'Design No. 1', corresponds approximately to the two previous plans. It gives an idea of how radically Soane intended to make over the College chapel here and in all his subsequent designs (compare these with Nos. 2 and 3). The tower and the pitched roof are to be flattened and the Gothic chancel window at the east end to be replaced with two of the Jacobean cross windows, which have been adopted throughout the complex in accordance with the wishes of the College authorities. The wall height of this remodelled south façade of the chapel block (about 30 feet), dictates the height of the entire complex with the exception of the two 'gatehouses'.

Soane has not applied a Classical order around his new quadrangle, preferring the austere rhythm of windows over the bare, shallow-arched openings of his arcade. The mausoleum here is a simple, two-storey cubic structure with clerestory windows, attached to the chapel as Bourgeois had wished. Since the previous sheet the Gallery has been moved from the south to the west side of the new quadrangle, opposite the entrance, as can be detected by its three large skylights. It must be assumed here and in three subsequent views (Nos. 17, 19 and 21, SM 65/4/08, 10 and 12) that the Gallery occupies the first floor above the ground floor arcade.

17

Dulwich College and Gallery: Design No. 1, Drawing No. 3. Perspective View

Soane Office

May 1811, pencil and watercolour, 32.4 × 47 cm

Inscr. 'No. III/Dulwich College/Design No. 1/ The Mausoleum placed with the Gallery/ LI Fields/May 1811'

SM 65/4/08

Dated May 1811, Soane inscribed this later perspective view 'Design No. 1' and inserted it accordingly within his sequence of presentation drawings for the College. This design is a variation on the previous one, without the 'gatehouses' along the College Road façade. The location of the mausoleum is unclear but the inscription – 'placed with the Gallery' – suggests that it is to run off its west side, as in the next drawing. The simplified Gallery range is now articulated by eleven identical bays. Here and in the previous view the Gallery is top lit, which means that its side windows were probably blind. The regular arcade here would presumably have run around two and a half sides of the quadrangle, as shown in the plan, No. 14.

18

Dulwich College and Gallery: Design No. 2, Drawing No. 4. Plan

Soane Office

April 1811, pencil, brown ink, and grey and pink wash, 35.2 × 31.7 cm

Inscr. 'No. IIII/Dulwich College/Plan No. 2/ Chapel/Porch/Tower/Gallery/April 1811'

SM 65/4/09

In his 'Design No. 2' for the new building Soane proposes an 'H' plan. The Gallery is placed on a north-south axis, connecting the remodelled chapel block to the north with a new wing, some 167 feet to the south. The plan of the Gallery here, with the mausoleum projecting from the centre of its west façade, loosely resembles the final design. On the east façade of the Gallery Soane places a substantial porch, like the one seen in the elevation of 4 April 1811 (No. 12, SM 65/4/28).

19

Dulwich College and Gallery: Design No. 2, Drawing No. 5. Perspective View

G Bailey

17 April 1811, pencil and watercolour, 32.3 × 46.8 cm

Inscr. 'Dulwich College/Design No. 2/ No. V/Lincolns Inn Fields/17 April 1811'

SM 65/4/10

This perspective view shows a version of Soane's H-plan, without the Gallery porch.

The mausoleum is probably hidden behind the Gallery block as in the previous plan. As in No. 17 (Design No. 1, SM 65/4/08), the Gallery seems to occupy the first floor above an open arcade, though now it is shortened to a seven-bay block, projecting forward slightly from the two towers at either end. It looks as if Soane intended to turn the existing tower of the chapel into a connecting lobby for his new Gallery.

20

Dulwich College and Gallery: Design No. 3, Drawing No. 6. Plan

Soane Office

April 1811, black ink, with pink, green, and grey wash, 35.4 × 51.9 cm

Inscr: 'No. VI/Dulwich College/Design No. 3 / Plan No. 3/Tower/Porch/Chapel/April 1811'

SM 65/4/11

This cross plan (Soane's 'Design No. 3') is generated by preserving the same part of the College (the south wing) and running the two new blocks north and south from its central axis, with the tower and porch as connecting lobbies. On the north side this would have meant demolishing the old east and west wings and creating the new block at the centre of the College quadrangle. The remodelling of the College chapel has here gone further than in previous examples: it looks as if Soane intends to run the Doric piers (seen in No. 4) all the way round the chapel. The locations of the Gallery and mausoleum are not specified. A copy of this plan dated 1822 is in the Victoria and Albert Museum (V&A 3307.111).

Soane's idea for this cross plan may derive from James Wyatt's (1746–1813) plan of Fonthill Abbey, built for William Beckford between 1795 and 1807.

21

Dulwich College and Gallery: Design No. 3, Drawing No 7. Perspective View

Soane Office

April 1811?, pencil and watercolour, 32 × 47.5 cm

Inscr. 'No. VII/Dulwich College/Design No. 3'

SM 65/4/12

The new wings here, running to the north and south (right and left), are based on the original west wing of the College (see No. 8, SM 65/4/03). Though the new blocks have the same Jacobean windows and the same pattern of three alternately recessed and projecting bays, their effect is transformed by an arcaded ground floor and a flat roof.

22

Design for the Entrance Façade of the Gallery

G Bailey or *GA Underwood*

29 April 1811, pencil, brown ink and grey wash, 31.5 × 54 cm

Inscr. '29 April 1811/Dulwich/[in pencil 'PIETYRS' [?], and various calculations.

SM 65/4/30

This scaled drawing, dated 29 April 1811, picks up on the elevation of 4 April 1811 (No. 12, SM 65/4/28), except that here the difference between the glazed windows of the porch and the blind windows of the Gallery is clearly indicated. Soane seems especially concerned here with the attic storey. His pupil has excluded the central episode only for Soane to reinstate it in a slightly different form in brown ink. For the first time Soane introduces funereal imagery into the design: he has added urns over the entrance and, sketched in pencil above the projecting outer bay to the left, a structure which resembles an ancient stele. Soane was eventually to use such classical, funereal imagery on the exterior of the mausoleum. This drawing is a good example of Soane's method of exploring new ideas over his pupil's finished drawings. The height of this façade is here marked as 27 feet 9 inches and its width can be calculated at 154 feet.

23

Dulwich College and Gallery: Design No. 4, Drawing No. 8. Plan

Soane Office

May 1811, pencil, black ink and water-colour, 32.3 × 46.7 cm

Inscr: 'No.VIII/Dulwich College/Design No. 4/Skylightroom/Gallery/Mausoleum/ Lins. Inn Field/May 1811'

SM 65/4/13

In his 'Design No. 4', Soane proposes for the first time the idea of a complete, four-sided quadrangle, some 196 feet across, 60 feet wider in than No. 14 (SM 65/4/43). This is also the first time that Soane uses the regular piers from the north elevation of the existing chapel (see No. 9, SM 65/4/02) in order to articulate every part of this remodelled block and the opposite one replicating it to the south.

The mausoleum acts as a link between the east end of the College chapel and the Gallery and is balanced at the other end of the Gallery by a room with a skylight. The layout of the mausoleum – a circular space surrounded by columns and a rectangular tomb chamber – is similar to that which Soane had designed in 1807 for Bourgeois's house in Charlotte Street. On the east front of the Gallery Soane places a sizeable entrance porch from College Road which is echoed on the west side by an extra room for the Gallery. The Gallery's rectangular and circular skylights are here clearly shown.

24

Dulwich College and Gallery: Design Nos. 4 and 5, Drawing No. 10. Perspective View

Soane Office

May 1811, pencil and watercolour, 32.2 × 46.6 cm

Inscr: 'No. X/Dulwich College/Design No. 4 & 5/Lincolns Inn Fields/May 1811'

SM 65/4/15

This impressive perspective view is loosely related to the previous plan. It shows the complete quadrangle design and gives some idea of what the piers around the chapel block (discussed above) might look like. However the details of the east and west wings are obviously different. Soane here returns to an earlier idea (see No. 18, 'Design No. 2', SM 65/4/09) of placing the mausoleum on the west side of the Gallery. As a result of this decision Bourgeois's mausoleum becomes the focal point of Soane's new quadrangle. At this stage, however, there is nothing (apart from the skylight) to suggest that the outside of the mausoleum would look any different from the surrounding buildings.

The Gallery façade along College Road is a development of the 'porch-type' (see especially No. 22, SM 65/4/30) with the familiar Neo-Jacobean windows but without the urns on the attic. This is the first view of the complex to show the Gallery block obviously lower than the chapel; its height here appears consistent with the 27 feet 9 inches shown in the elevation, No. 22 (SM 65/4/30).

25

Dulwich College and Gallery: Design No. 5, Drawing No. 11. Plan

Soane Office

May 1811, pencil, black and brown ink, and grey and pink wash, 34 × 53 cm

Inscr. 'No. XI/Design No. 5/Chapel/ Mausoleum/Gallery/Entrance/Dulwich College/Lincolns Inns Field/May 1811'

SM 65/4/16

The lower half of this plan relates very closely to the previous view, except that Soane has changed the form of the skylights over the three central galleries from rectangular to circular. The west wing (at the top) was probably intended to look more as it did in the perspectival view, No. 16 (SM 65/4/07). Assuming the mausoleum remains as it appears in the previous design, it must have been intended to have a circular skylight over the burial area, as in Nos. 28 and 29 (V&A 3307.109 and SM F91). The quadrangle is now 200 feet wide.

26

The Interior of the Gallery: Design No. 5, Drawing No. 12. Perspective View

Soane Office

May 1811, pencil, brown ink and watercolour, 41.3 × 32.6 cm

Inscr: 'No. XII/Dulwich College/View of Gallery Design No. 5/Lincolns Inn Field/ May 1811'

SM 65/4/17

This first representation of the interior of the Gallery is entirely consistent with the previous plan, also marked 'Design No. 5'. Here Soane established his initial idea for Dulwich's influential enfilade, with its sequence of five undecorated arches. It is loosely modelled on the Shakespeare Gallery of 1788–9, designed by George Dance the Younger (1741–1825), with whom Soane trained as an architect. At this stage in the design the skylights are circular and rest on typically Soanean flattened sail vaults. Their geometry derives from slicing a square section out of a sphere of very large diameter (the larger the diameter the flatter the vault). To cover a room of rectangular plan, this square form requires an extra element at either end; these are made of flattened barrels vaults or sections of cylinders of similarly large diameters.

Even at this early stage, Soane conceived of the Dulwich galleries as red in colour, and hung with up to five tiers of paintings.

27

The Interior of the Gallery. Perspective View

Soane Office

May 1811?, watercolour, 26.3 × 27.5 cm

SM 65/4/14

This interior view of the Gallery is a reduced version of the previous drawing.

28

Section through the Gallery with a Single Storey Mausoleum

Soane Office

May 1811?, pen and ink, with brown, yellow and pink wash, 17 × 23.7 cm

V&A 3307.109

This spectacular section through the centre of the Gallery building corresponds to Soane's plan for 'Design No. 5' (No. 25, SM 65/4/16). The entrance porch is on the left; the simple doorway leads to one of the two side rooms. The Gallery is lit by a circular lantern resting on a sail vault, as in the two previous views, the end of the enfilade is closed by a simple door, with splayed surrounds of a type recommended by Vitruvius. To the right the interior of the mausoleum is shown for the first time. An austere fluted Greek Doric order (without bases) articulates the sunken space of the circular vestibule, with a shallow, coffered dome and rusticated walls. This severe space loosely recalls Joseph Bonomi's (1739–1808) Greek Doric painted ashlar interior of St James's Church, Great Packington, Warwickshire of 1789–90. At Dulwich, three steps lead up to the tomb chamber, lit from above by a circular lantern (see No. 24). There is clearly space here for three sarcophagi, resting on high rectangular bases, presumably to house Francis Bourgeois and his friends, Noël and Margaret Desenfans. A reduced copy of this section drawing, dated 1824, is also in the Victoria and Albert Museum (V&A 3307.110).

29

Interior Perspective of the Mausoleum

JM Gandy

1811, pen and ink and watercolour, 80 × 80 cm

Inscr. on the frame: 'Interior of Mausoleum. Dulwich College. (Sir John Soane, 1811)'

SM F91

This ideal view of the interior of the Dulwich mausoleum is consistent with the previous section, except in the form of the sarcophagi themselves. Soane described the effect he intended: 'a dull. religious light shews the Mausoleum in the full pride of funereal grandeur'. Its design, as Bourgeois requested in his will, is close to Soane's views of the Charlotte Street mausoleum of 1807. In the foreground two figures inspect the building's plan which is similar to that of Nos. 23 and 25 (SM 5/4/13 and SM 65/4/16) but corresponds to the previous section No. 28 (V&A

3307.109). This view is probably the 'View of a Mausoleum to the late Sir F. Bourgeois, Knt.' exhibited at the Royal Academy in 1811 (RA No. 880). It was later published in Soane's 'Designs for Public and Private Buildings' in 1828.

Soane's 'Designs Six to Eight': May 1811

30

Dulwich College and Gallery: Design No. 6. Plan

Soane Office

May 1811?, pencil, with pink and grey wash, 45.5 × 58.4 cm

Inscr. 'Design No. 6/Skylights' [in pencil on end galleries]

SM 65/4/42

The earlier finished part of this drawing shows a version of Soane's 'Design No. 6' which differs from No. 18 in its proportions: three blocks of identical length (147 feet) mark out a much wider H-shaped complex (208 feet rather than 167 feet across). This extra breathing space allows for linking arcades at either end of the Gallery. The positions of the porch and mausoleum have also been reversed.

On top of this drawing Soane has worked in pencil, pushing the Gallery back to the west and creating a stair well in the central projecting entrance lobby. As is only suggested in earlier examples (Nos. 16, 17, 19 and 21, SM 65/4/07, 08, 10 and 12) the Gallery here is clearly planned to run along the first floor of the block with the 'old women under' as Soane put it in his diary. In other sketches on this sheet, Soane begins to develop ideas for 'Design No. 8' (No. 34, SM 65/4/40), in which the new building is linked to the old buildings by a quadrant arcade.

31

Dulwich College: Ground Floor Plan of Two-Storey Gallery Block showing Almshouses and Mausoleum (Gallery above)

Soane Office

May 1811?, pencil, with pink and grey wash, 45 × 58.3 cm

SM 65/4/39

This plan works up the ideas of the previous sheet: the Gallery is set back behind the line of the old west wing (now to be retained) and it is linked to the College by an arcade running across its entire length. In this ground floor plan, the rooms of the almshouses are clearly marked out, as are the stairs up to the Gallery. The lobby area in the centre of the Gallery block, with four free-standing piers, may have been inspired by that under Wren's library at Trinity College, Cambridge. The mausoleum continues to be placed on the east side of the Gallery as a focal point for the quadrangle that Soane still envisaged.

32

Dulwich College and Gallery: Design No. 7. Plan of the Gallery Block

J Buxton

25 May 1811, pencil, with grey and white wash, 45 × 58 cm

Inscr: 'Dulwich College 25 May 1811/Design No. 7/Arcade/Gallery/Vestibule/Chamber/Living Room [on almshouses]/Lincolns Inn Fields/25 May 1811'

SM 65/4/41

Possibly drawn in response to a visit the day before to the Master of the College, this design contains all the crucial elements of the definitive solution. The new building combines almshouses and Gallery in one single-storey block; it clearly belongs with the College and lines up with the old west wing and yet requires little demolition. Old and new are linked by a straight arcade which joins the Gallery on its central north-south axis, rather than passing in front, as in the previous drawing.

This sheet was drawn by John Buxton, Soane's pupil from 1809 to 1814. After leaving Soane's Office, Buxton (like Basevi) travelled in Italy (1816–7); references in Basevi's letters home record that Buxton proposed abandoning architecture for sculpture.

33
Plan of the Gallery
Soane Office
May 1811?, pencil and brown wash,
45 × 58 cm
Inscr. (in Soane's hand?): '6 × 14/12 – 10 women/5 women each 2 rooms 1 matron (?) 3 rooms/also … [?]… 5 kitchen/…[?]… dining room/Kitchen'
SM 65/4/38

Based on the previous plan, this sheet shows Soane working on top of a pupil's drawing to try to find extra almshouse space. In the pupil's hand, space for four alms women is provided; the College wanted to house five and a matron. Soane explores how he can extend his Gallery block to the west.

34
Dulwich College and Gallery: Design No. 8. Plan
Soane Office
May 1811?, pencil and grey wash,
45.5 × 58 cm
Inscr. 'Lincolns Inn Field/Dulwich/Design No. 8/Arcade/Entrance/The Picture Gallery/ Mausoleum/A [at the building's corner points]'
SM 65/4/40

Soane's 'Design No. 8' differs from 'Design No. 7' only in that the Gallery block is set further back towards the west and is connected to the College buildings by quadrant arcades. This plan would have created a grander, U-shaped complex – had Soane been allowed to build his new south block – but it would have involved the demolition of more of the south-west corner of the College than the definitive solution.

35
West Elevation of the Gallery Block
Soane Office
May 1811, watercolour, 33.6 × 53 cm
Inscr: 'Dulwich College/May 1811'
SM 65/4/20

This is the first elevation to show the rear Gallery Road façade of Soane's Gallery, and is consistent with the three previous plans. The main entrance to the Gallery is in the central block, framed by pilaster-panels of no recognisable order and crowned by a pediment. The round arches lead to small porch spaces with doors to the almshouses opening off either side.

This design is similar to Soane's first ideas for the Gallery façade when it was on College Road (see No. 12, dated 4 April 1811, SM 65/4/28). In this later design, however, the entrance vestibule is encased by the almshouses to each side and is articulated on the façade by only a slight projection. Unlike future designs the whole of the almshouse block here is lower than the Gallery behind – in other words the building would have looked like an oversized pair of steps.

The Approved Design: 12 July 1811

36
Plan of the Gallery and College Buildings
G Bailey or *J Buxton*
10 July 1811, pencil, with grey and pink wash,
46 × 58.5 cm
Inscr. 'AAAA Apartments/for old women./ At Dulwich 12 July 1811/Present, Master /Mr Corry/Mr Douch [?]/Mr Smith – saw and app[roved] but/was engaged/to dinner at/Clapham/Mr Jullian/Mr Druce/This general plan/App[roved] & also est[ablished]/ Dulwich College/Entrance/Gallery/The Picture Gallery/The Mausoleum/Great Quadrangle/Arcade/Chapel/Lincolns Inn Fields 10 [amended 12] July, 1811'
SM 65/4/37

This general site plan blocks out the usage of the new building, without showing the exact division of rooms. This is the only drawing Soane brought to the meeting with the College on 12 July, showing an arcade across the east front of the Gallery, though he added one in pencil to the next plan, No. 37. This idea of the arcade is developed from his previous two-storey proposal, 'Design No. 6' (No. 31, SM 65/4/39). In every other respect this design is a development of his 'Design No. 7', with only small differences such as the westward extension of the end bays of the almshouse façade, as initially sketched in on No. 33 (SM 65/4/38).

Soane's pencil, presumably at work during the meeting, here sketches out a new, less ostentatious position for the mausoleum at the end of the south range of the old College and in line with the Gallery. Perhaps because of its asymmetry, these ideas were taken no further. It is interesting at this stage that there is no suggestion of moving the mausoleum to its present position on the west façade.

37

Plan of the Gallery

G Bailey or *J Buxton*

10 July 1811, pencil, black and brown ink, with pink and blue wash, 33.1 × 51.7 cm

Inscr. 'Dulwich College/Plan of the Principal Storey/Lincolns Inn Fields/10 July 1811/ This plan exh [?] on 12 July 1811/& Finally appr.d by the/Master/Mr Corry/Mr Douch [?]/Mr Smith/Mr Jullian/Mr Druce/ with the addition of an arcade/as shown in the general plan./Mausoleum/sarcoph./Skylight/ Picture Gallery/Arcade/Porch/Vestibule/The optimum length of the Gallery 144, 6 [crossed out and corrected to] 152 [ft] out and out' [and various calculations].

SM 65/4/34

This is the first plan or view that Soane produced for the project with north to the left rather than the right. In other words, everything so far has been seen as if from College Road; this is seen as if viewed from Gallery Road. The College authorities were evidently so confused by this that they decided to look at it upside down. They also approved the addition in pencil of the arcade across the east façade, fitting neatly between the Mausoleum and the Gallery.

The principle change between this design and the previous group (see especially Nos. 32–35) concerns the end bays of the almshouse façade. Not only do they jut westwards (as mentioned in connection with the previous plan), they are also narrower (with a single window to the west) and, most important of all, they are now intended to be two storeys high. In this way Soane created the space to accommodate six alms women. The arcade entrances to the Gallery and the porches to the north and south ends of the almshouses appear on this drawing for the last time.

The interior proportions of the Gallery here begin to resemble those built. All five rooms are roughly the same width (though the central one is fractionally wider). The dimensions written in ink – 18 feet by 22 feet, 40 feet by 21 feet 9 inches, 20 feet 6 inches square – were presumably added in the meeting. They were subsequently crossed out in pencil and replaced by new dimensions which correspond exactly with those built: the two large galleries are marked 40 feet by 20 feet and the middle and end rooms 20 feet 9 inches square (in his later plans Soane rounded this figure up to 21 feet square). In brown ink Soane gives his 'optimum length of the Gallery' as 144 feet 6 inches, again in pencil this figure is corrected to 148 feet 3 inches; a further 3 feet 9 in is added to account for wall thickness, giving Soane a new optimum length: '152 ft out and out' – just two foot short of the built length of the Gallery.

38

Plan of the Upper Storey of the Gallery

G Bailey or *J Buxton*

10 July 1811, black ink, with pink, blue, and yellow wash, 33 × 52.5 cm

Inscr. 'Dulwich College/Plan of the Upper Storey/Mausoleum/Slate Roof/Lead Flash [on all skylights]/Staircase/14' by 10' [almshouse chamber]/14 feet square [almshouse living room]/Lincolns Inn Field/10 July 1811/ At Dulwich 12 July 1811/Plan app[rove]d'

SM 65/4/33

This plan shows the arrangement of the upper storey of the end bay almshouses and the Gallery. The skylights are here still circular for the square rooms and rectangular for the others; all these eventually became octagonal.

39

West Elevation of the Gallery

G Bailey

10 July 1811, pencil and watercolour, 33.2 × 52.6 cm

Inscr. 'Dulwich College/Entrance Front/

next the road/The Picture Gallery/Top part of cornice stone/stone plinth/Brick pilasters/Lincolns Inn Fields/10 July 1811'
SM 65/4/21

This elevation is essentially the same as No. 35 (SM 65/4/20, dated May 1811), except that Soane has had to accommodate the two-storey almshouse block at either end. This bay now looks more like the ends of the east façade (see No. 40, SM 65/4/23), with the same articulation by means of render pilaster-bands. Soane also omitted the balustrade seen in No. 35, perhaps to save money. Elements of the building to be built in stone, such as the cornice, are marked on this drawing.

40

East Elevation of the Gallery

G Bailey
10 July 1811, pen and brown ink, and watercolour, 32.8 × 52 cm
Inscr. 'Dulwich College/Lincolns Inn Fields/10 July 1811/: This elevation must be/altered to admit the/arcade as settled/12 July 1811/Section through/the lobby between the Mausoleum/and the Great Gallery/Entrance front next the/Great Quadrangle/Upper part of cornice stone/stone plinth/Brick pilasters'
SM 65/4/23

In this east elevation, Soane slices through the mausoleum in order to show a section through its vestibule. The familiar Jacobean windows (presumably blind) remain the only non-classical element in the design which now has a pediment and acroteria on the skyline. This elevation also has annotations noting that the plinth and cornice are to be of stone and the remainder of brick.

From Approved Design to Foundation Stone: 12 July to 19 October 1811

41

East Elevation and Second Storey Plan of the Gallery

G Bailey, GA Underwood, or *G Basevi*
17 July 1811, black ink, with pink and red wash, 61.1 × 96.4 cm
Inscr. 'God's Gift College in Dulwich/July 17 1811'
SM 15/1/05

Five days after his meeting at the College on 12 July 1811, Soane's pupils produced this radically new design for the east façade. The single storey mausoleum has been moved to the west side of the Gallery, as first proposed in April (see No. 18, SM 65/4/09) where it was eventually built. Without the mausoleum, the east façade acquires a dramatic austerity, with an arcade of almost industrial simplicity, recalling Robert Adam's Adelfi Dock on the Thames of 1768-72. Soane here proposes to light the Gallery with a clerestory instead of skylights. The form of these windows, with their depressed arched top, is similar to that of the arcade in previous projects (see Nos. 16, 17, 19 and 21, SM 65/4/07, 08, 10 and 12).

Unlike previous designs this starkly rectangular façade is made up of simple whole-number proportions: the length is six times the height; the screens at the end are exactly square, which means that the central section is made up of four squares. The interiors here are also a sequence of squares and double-squares; given the external height of the building they could have been cubes and double-cubes, as at Inigo Jones's Wilton House.

42

East Elevation of the Gallery (half)

Soane Office
July 1811?, pencil and grey wash, 47.5 × 68 cm
SM 65/4/54

This detailed version of the previous design explores some variations, such as the elimination of the pediments and the inclusion of a pitched roof. The pilasters here are even more minimal than in previous designs: presumably the shafts are to be brick, with a stone plinth below and a single triglyph in the stone frieze above.

43

Plan of the Gallery

G Bailey, GA Underwood, or *G Basevi*
17 July 1811, pencil and watercolour, 62 × 96 cm
Inscr. 'Dulwich College/Lincolns Inns Fields/

July 17th 1811'
SM 15/1/01

All three plans in this group (Nos. 43–5) show the mausoleum back on the east façade, but include features, such as the arcade, agreed at the meeting of 12 July. Soane did not revisit the idea of placing the mausoleum on the west front again until 24 October 1811.

Ever since May (see especially Nos. 35 and 39, SM 65/4/20 and 21) Soane had considered his almshouse façade as divided into five blocks – two ends (now double-storey), two 'cottages' inside, and the vestibule for the Gallery in the middle. In this plan and the next Soane moves the four almshouse entrances to narrow bays separating (and helping to articulate) these five blocks. This plan and the next are rare examples orientated with north to the left (or as seen from Gallery Road).

44
Plan of the Gallery
G Bailey, GA Underwood, G Basevi,
or *J Buxton*
19 July 1811, pencil and watercolour,
62 × 96.3 cm
Inscr: 'Dulwich College/Lincolns Inns Fields/19th July 1811'
SM 15/1/02

This plan differs little from the previous, except in reducing the width of the Gallery vestibule and adding some cross-shaped projections to the mausoleum. This drawing is consistent with the elevation of 29 July 1811 (No. 49, SM 15/1/04).

45
Half Plan of the Gallery
Soane Office
July 1811?, black and brown ink with pink wash, 58 × 70 cm
SM 65/4/62

An enlarged version of the previous, with slight changes to the Gallery vestibule area and the alignment of doors within the almshouses, this plan also appears to correspond to the elevation of 29 July 1811 (No. 49, SM 15/1/04). What appears to be a chimney flue has been inserted at the centre of the west wall of the largest gallery.

46
Perspective View of the East Façade with Mausoleum
John Soane
21 July 1811, pencil, with grey wash,
28.3 × 44 cm
Inscr. 'View from the great quadrangle of Dulwich College,/shewing [sic] the proposed design for the Mausoleum of/ the late Sir Francis Bourgeois, & the Gallery/ to contain the Pictures left by him to Dulwich College/L I Fields/21 July 1811'
SM 65/4/25

This original Soane watercolour and the two studio views that follow are his first attempts to show the Mausoleum fully developed. Nos. 16 and 24 (SM 65/4/07 and SM 65/4/15) show a previous and utterly different design. All three views are consistent with the last two plans (Nos. 44 and 45). In essence, if not in detail, this is the mausoleum as built, with its low, columned rotunda leading to a high lanterned burial chamber which is surrounded on the outside by three imposingly framed false doors. The funereal urns are already present, as is the characteristic 'Telephone Box' cupola. Soane previously used this motif in 1806 on the funerary monument of Samuel Bosanquet. This mausoleum design is unique in having an Ionic (rather than a primitive Doric) order.

47
Perspective View of the East Façade with Mausoleum
G Bailey, GA Underwood, J Buxton
or *G Basevi*
22 July 1811, watercolour, 30.5 × 45.5 cm
Inscr. 'Dulwich College/Lincolns Inn Fields/ July 22 1811'
SM 65/4/26

This studio variant of the previous view shows some alterations (later abandoned), principally the expansion of the Soanean cupola form to cover the whole lantern. In the top left corner of the sheet is a preliminary study, in Soane's hand, for the urn design.

48

Perspective View of the East Façade with Mausoleum

Soane Office
July 1811?, pencil and watercolour,
29.5 × 44 cm
SM 65/4/27

The mausoleum here combines features of both Nos. 46 and 47.

49

East and West Elevations of the Gallery

GA Underwood
29 July 1811, pencil and water colour,
62.1 × 96 cm
Inscr. 'Dulwich College/Front Next the Great Quadrangle/Front Next the Entrance Court/Lincoln Inn Fields/29 July 1811'
SM 15/1/04

Drawn by George Underwood, these elevations show Soane's ideas for the almshouses (see also No. 50, SM 65/4/22) as well as the impact of Soane's new mausoleum design. Loosely based on the last of the three previous variants (No. 48, SM 65/4/27), Soane here creates a more emphatic rusticated block as the heart of his mausoleum design. It seems clear that the entire structure is intended to be built of stone. The almshouse windows derive from those Soane developed for his clerestory lights earlier in July 1811 (see No. 42, SM 65/ 4/54).

50

West Elevation of the Gallery

Soane Office
August 1811?, pencil and watercolour,
32.6 × 52.6 cm
Inscr. 'Dulwich College/August 1811'
SM 65/4/22

Dated August 1811, this elevation (like No. 49, SM 15/1/04) is consistent with the plan of 19 July 1811 (No. 44, SM 15/1/2). Everything here is clearly drawn as brickwork, except for the attic which is coloured to suggest it should be rendered. Unlike the previous elevation, Soane has here divided up his lower almshouses into two 'cottages', with three windows each. Each block is articulated by the position of the doors, which are set below decorative panels (sketched in on the previous design) in a slightly recessed bay. Soane has also set the almshouse windows and the undecorated Gallery doorway into shallow arches, to introduce a further play of light and shadow and to give depth to the façade.

51

East-West Section through the Gallery and Mausoleum

Soane Office
July or August 1811?, pencil, grey and brown wash, 42.5 × 59 cm
SM 65/4/57

Though undated, this east-west section generally corresponds with other designs in this group. The almshouses to the left match the previous elevation and the following plan. The Gallery appears as it did in the internal view of May 1811 (No. 26, SM 65/4/17), though now the enfilade is closed with a window rather than a door. On this sheet Soane has also sketched proposals for what look like huge clerestory windows under the vault. Soane returned to a similar idea in late October 1811 (No. 57, SM 65/4/35).

We see here for the first time the internal arrangement of Soane's new mausoleum, which is a variant of the 'wide-cupola' design seen in the Soane office watercolour No. 47, (SM 65/4/26). Access from the arcade leads through a rusticated vestibule with a ring of unfluted Greek Doric columns to the burial chamber itself, which is lit by a tall lantern, with three round topped windows. If this section corresponds to the plan of 7 August 1811 (No. 52, SM 65/4/31), the back of this burial chamber opens directly onto Soane's 'Great Quadrangle'.

52

Plan of the Gallery and College Buildings

G Bailey, GA Underwood or *G Basevi*
7 August 1811, pencil, black ink and pink wash, 33 x51.8 cm
Inscr. 'Dulwich College/Lincolns Inn Fields/August 7 1811'

SM 65/4/31

This plan shows the same design as No. 45 (SM 65/4/62) but in the wider context of the College, as Soane wished to re-design it. Three blocks of near identical length enclose the widest quadrangle Soane envisaged for Dulwich – 228 feet across.

53

Plan of the Upper Storey of the Gallery
G Bailey, GA Underwood, G Basevi or *C Tyrell*
7 August 1811, pencil, with pink, yellow and grey wash, 32 × 51.5 cm
Inscr. 'Dulwich College/Lincolns Inn Fields/ August 7, 1811'
SM 65/4/32

This plan corresponds to the previous sheet also dated 7 August 1811. It shows that at this stage Soane still proposed circular skylights for the square galleries. For the first time the lantern of the mausoleum is represented on an upper storey plan (compare No. 38, SM 65/ 4/33, dated 10 July 1811, and No. 41, SM 15/1/05 dated 17 July 1811).

54

Perspective View of the East Façade with Mausoleum
G Bailey, GA Underwood or *G Basevi*
8 August 1811, watercolour, 36 × 52.2 cm
Inscr. 'Dulwich College/Lincolns Inn Fields/ August 8, 1811'
SM 65/4/36

Clearly related to the three perspective views of 21–22 July (Nos. 46-48 SM 65/4/25, 26, 27), this sheet tries out a new mausoleum design, capping the lantern with an elongated version of the scroll motif previously used for the entrance portals. This solution recalls the *stele* on which Piranesi inscribed a dedication to Robert Adam in his reconstruction view of the Via Appia, the frontispiece to the second volume of the *Antichità Romane* of which Soane had several copies. The portals are now capped with half-cylinders, presumably intended to suggest sarcophagi.

55

East Elevation of the Gallery with Mausoleum
Soane Office
August 1811, watercolour, 33.2 × 52.4 cm
Inscr. 'Dulwich College/August 1811'
SM 65/4/19

This elevation matches the design of the previous sheet and makes it clear that the lower storey of the mausoleum was to be made of brick, while the upper half was to be of stone, as was the case with the mausoleum as executed. Symbolic funereal serpents – which shed their skin as the resurrected soul sheds its body – appear here for the first time.

56

Perspective View of the East Façade with Mausoleum
JM Gandy?
1811-12?, watercolour, 44 × 58 cm
Inscr. 'View of a Design for a Mausoleum to the Memory of Sir Francis Bourgeois/ and a Gallery for the reception of his Collection of Pictures bequeathed to Dulwich College'.
SM 15/2/02

Exhibited at the Royal Academy in 1812 (RA No. 810), when work on the Gallery was well under way, this perspective watercolour is based on the elevation of 29 July 1811 (No. 49, SM 15/1/4). It differs only in showing octagonal skylights appearing above the parapet. Though it fits into the design sequence at this point, this watercolour may have been executed later (in early 1812) in order to show the public a design that Soane was especially proud of, even though it had been abandoned by then.

The Mausoleum Moves to the West Side of the Galley: October to November 1811

57

Perspective View of the West Façade
G Bailey, GA Underwood or *G Basevi*
24 October 1811, watercolour, 35.2 × 52.2 cm
Inscr. 'Lincolns Inn Fields. Oct 24, 1811'

SM 65/4/35

This perspective view takes the mausoleum design of 8 August 1811 (No. 54 SM 65/4/36) and bolts it onto the centre of the almshouse façade design as seen in No. 50 (SM 65/4/ 22). There are of course variations: more conventional sarcophagi replace the strange cylinders on the mausoleum, and clerestory windows reappear on the Gallery, elongated five-light versions of those first designed on 17 July 1811 (Nos. 41, 42 and 51; SM 15/1/05; SM 65/4/54 and 57).

58

Perspective View of the West Façade

G Bailey or *GA Underwood*

28 October 1811, pencil and watercolour, 35.7 × 52 cm

Inscr. 'John Soane Archt./Lincolns Inn Fields/ Oct 28 1811'

SM 65/4/18

This perspective view shows the same design as the previous one but with individual clerestory windows, exactly as they appeared on the designs of 17 July (Nos. 41 and 42, SM 15/1/05 and SM 65/4/54).

59

Plan of the Gallery

Soane Office

1811?, pencil and black ink with pink wash, 30.1 × 48.4 cm

SM 65/4/49

This plan, together with the following two, works at the detail of inserting the mausoleum between the two cottage blocks, in place of the vestibule seen in No. 52 of 7 August 1811 (SM 65/4/31).

60

Half Plan of the Gallery

Soane Office

1811?, pencil and brown ink and pink, with orange wash, 46.5 × 64 cm

SM 65/4/59

This plan is identical to the former except that Soane has added a small circular skylight over the narrow passage way between the mausoleum and the almshouses. The Gallery interiors here are all squares and double-squares.

61

Half Plan of the Gallery

Soane Office

1811?, pencil, with pink and grey wash, 48 × 68 cm

SM 65/4/60

This plan is identical to the previous one except that Soane has added paired columns and half columns at the opening of each arch between the galleries of the main enfilade, presumably to create Serlianas, in an arrangement reminiscent of Hubert Robert's 1796 project for the remodelling of the Grand Galerie of the Louvre.

A Porch for the East Façade of the Gallery and Other Designs: October 1811 to April 1812

62

Long and Cross Sections Through Gallery

Soane Office

5 March 1812, pencil with yellow wash, 45.2 × 65.5 cm

Inscr. 'March 5, 1812'

SM 65/4/58

The last we saw of the skylights was on 7 August 1811 (No. 53, 65/4/32) when they were either circular or rectangular. In this section Soane has come up with the idea of octagonal skylights throughout, as in the final building, though here with more delicate and rounded vertical lights. Soane also gives the first indication here of the Gallery's distinctive vaulting system. The geometry of these vaults is generated by 'cutting the corner' (at an angle of 45°) between the vertical of the wall and the horizontal of the base of the roof lights. Lunettes (a form like a semicircular blind window) are cut into this sloping plaster, creating a pattern like a traditional groin vault. The Dulwich arrangement of vaults supporting skylights is similar to that created in 1716–9 by Sir John Vanbrugh (1664–1726) for the Great Kitchen at St James's Palace.

As we would expect from recent plans (for example No. 59) Soane is here interested in creating a sequence of cubes and double-cubes, even if the vault shaves off the edges of these perfect forms. Soane marks up the height at the base of the skylight in two of the square rooms as 21 feet – exactly the same as their dimensions in plan.

63

Half Plan of the Gallery

Soane Office

1811, flap added early 1812?, pencil, black and brown ink, with pink wash, 65.7 × 68.7 cm

Inscr. 'Dulwich College/1811/Arcade/ Picture Gallery/Chapel/Mausoleum'

SM 65/4/61

In this plan, dated 1811, the skylights are clearly marked as octagonal structures, as seen in the previous drawing and in No. 56 (SM 15/2/02). At a later date – possibly in early 1812 – a flap was glued onto this plan, showing the plan of the new east porch. Around the mausoleum Soane sketches the outline of the rounded plinth as well as the cylindrical altars seen in Gandy's famous 1812 view of the Gallery, (No. 82, SM 15/2/3). Several recent images of the mausoleum have seemed to show a door at the rear; here the three sarcophagi are back in their definitive positions (as in No. 37, SM 65/4/34).

64

Outline Plan of the Gallery

Soane Office

Early 1812?, pencil and grey wash, 51.5 × 66.5 cm

SM 65/4/63

This outline plan of the Gallery proposes placing a porch on the east side of the Gallery; though obviously intended to balance the mausoleum on the west side, it is in fact slightly wider to fit into the rhythm of the arcade.

65

Perspective View of the East Façade

John Soane?

Early 1812?, pencil with grey wash, 27.5 × 29.5 cm

SM 65/4/24

Drawn in the same media and style as the first view of the mausoleum, dated 21 July 1811 (No. 46, SM 65/4/25), this sheet may be in Soane's own hand. It shows the porch to be no more than a version of the mausoleum minus its lantern. This view is consistent with the previous plan.

66

Elevation of the East Façade

Soane Office

Early 1812?, pencil, 30 × 48.5 cm

SM 65/4/52

Essentially the elevation to correspond with the previous view, this leaves a space where the porch should be and reverts to an earlier form for the skyline of the end bays (compare No. 42, SM 65/4/54).

67

Elevation of the West Façade

Soane Office

Early 1812?, pencil, 30 × 48.5 cm

SM 65/4/51

This sheet forms a pair with the previous elevation: both are drawn in the same style on the same size and type of paper and both are unfinished. The design here is essentially that shown in the view of 28 October 1811 (No. 58, SM 65/4/18), but with panels instead of windows in the Gallery attic and an incomplete mausoleum.

68

Elevations of the East and West Façades

G Bailey, GA Underwood or *G Basevi*

13 April 1812, pencil and watercolour, 50 × 71 cm

Inscr. 'Elevation of the Entrance Front/ Elevation of the Front Next the Road/ Lincolns Inn Fields/April 13th 1812'

SM 15/1/03

These elevations show the proposals that Soane developed in the three previous sheets (SM 65/4/24, 52 and 51) now worked up into finished designs. The east porch is noticeably wider than the west mausoleum and designed not to interrupt the rhythm of the arcade. The mausoleum is a lower version of that seen in the elevation of 29 July 1811 (No. 49, SM 15/1/4), with the traditional sarcophagi recently introduced. We see here also the octagonal skylights already developed in No. 62 (SM 65/4/58). In this elevation the pediments often seen over the end bays are finally abandoned in favour of horizontal panels. As in previous examples, the length of these façades is six times their height.

The North and East Façades of the Gallery: Early 1811

69

Half Elevation of the East Façade

G Bailey, GA Underwood or *G Basevi*
13 April 1812, pencil, black and brown ink, with grey and pink wash, 46.6 × 66.2 cm
Inscr. 'Dulwich College/Elevation of half the Entrance Front/Lincolns Inn Fields/ April 13, 1812'
SM 65/4/56

This definitive elevation and section of the east façade uses ideas already put to paper, notably in No. 66 (SM 65/4/52). To the left a rough sketch for the chimney design is drawn in pencil on the skyline. Soane's own measurements reveal the proportions discussed above: from numbers given here we can deduce that the whole façade measures 154 feet (exactly the length of the Gallery as built); the end bay is marked up as 25 feet 6 inches across and measures the same in height. (For a façade width exactly six times its height this figure should be 25 feet 8 inches, Soane here is working almost exactly to a system of numerical proportions).

70

Half Elevation of the East Façade

Soane Office
1812?, pencil, black ink and grey wash,
42 × 66 cm
SM 65/4/55

This dimensioned drawing is a copy of the previous sheet.

71

Elevation and Section of the North Façade of the Gallery

Soane Office
April 1812, black ink with pink and grey wash, 48 × 68 cm
Inscr. 'Dulwich College/Elevation of one of the Ends/Lincolns Inn Fields April 1812'
SM 65/4/53

This is the first time we have been given a clear idea of what the end façades of the Gallery were to look like. This elevation corresponds to plan No. 63 (SM 65/4/61), a comparison which shows how clever Soane has been at creating the illusion of symmetry for a façade which covers an asymmetrical building. It is not the central window which lines up with the Gallery enfilade, as you might expect, but the window immediately to its left. This central window and others on this mendacious façade are intended to be blind.

72

Elevation of the North Façade of the Gallery

Soane Office
April 1812?, pencil, with grey wash,
30 × 48 cm
SM 65/4/50

This sheet is a reduced copy of the previous.

The West Façade and Gallery Roof-Line. Real and Ideal Designs: April to July 1812

73

Section and Elevation of the Mausoleum

G Basevi
29 April 1812, pencil and black ink, with grey and pink wash, 68.5 × 48.3 cm
Inscr. 'LI Fields/29 April 1812'
SM 65/4/48

The design of the mausoleum here is similar to that seen previously in No. 68 (SM 15/1/03), except that it has been stripped of decorative mouldings and is now crowned by a single urn (with others indicated in pencil). This drawing is fully dimensioned and close to the mausoleum as built.

74
Elevation of the Lantern
Soane Office
May 1812?, pencil and grey wash,
38 × 25 cm
SM 65/4/44

A small step away from the previous elevation, this sheet is a finished design for the lantern as built. Sketched in Soane's hand is the proposal to elongate the lantern, as seen in Gandy's perspective views of the Gallery (Nos. 82 and 3, SM 15/2/03 and 04).

75
Perspective View of the Mausoleum
G Basevi
11 May 1812, watercolour, 87.7 × 68.5 cm
Inscr. 'May 11 1812'
SM 15/2/07

Broadly consistent with the two previous designs, this perspective view shows a structure similar to that built, even down to the use of brick for the lower storey and stone for the lantern. It differs primarily in the welcoming entrances, with steps leading up from the rectangular to the arched apertures, which are like those of Soane's design of 21 July 1811 (No. 46, SM 65/4/25). These were eventually replaced by unwelcoming – indeed deliberately excluding – false doors beneath an arch.

76
Perspective View of the Mausoleum
Soane Office
May 1812?, pencil with grey wash,
47.5 × 35 cm
SM 65/4/45

Related to the previous design, this view shows a structure closer to that finally built, with arched 'entrances' to the mausoleum. It differs only in decorative details: lions (instead of urns) decorate the top corners of the lantern, and the windows have three large round-topped lights (instead of the present rectangular lattice).

77
Elevation of the West Façade
Soane Office
May 1812?, pencil and grey wash,
55 × 66.5 cm
SM 65/5/03

The measured elements on this sheet shows the west façade of the Gallery essentially as built. Soane's pencil additions, however, suggest some interesting departures: for the only almshouse window illustrated Soane has returned to the Jacobean design which featured in so many of the early projects (see for example No. 12, SM 65/4/28 or No. 16, SM 65/4/07). Here, however, they are set within a stone pedimented frame, reminiscent of an antique *stele*. A very similar form appears in the arch of the mausoleum: this may be a door similar to the one built, or another example of the *stele* form as occurs in the following designs.

78
Perspective View of the Mausoleum with a Plan of the Gallery and Views of the East and West Façades Inserted Below
R Chantrell or *G Basevi*
23 May 1812, pencil, with grey, pink, orange and yellow wash, 60 × 48 cm
Inscr. 'View of the Garden Front/View of the Principal Front/May 23, 1812'
SM 65/4/46

This design makes the mausoleum appear detached from the Gallery, presumably for dramatic effect. Close to the final design, it varies only in decorative features, such as the addition of a Roman altar in the central arch and the exchanging of the lantern's uppermost urn for a flaming altar recalling that on the Evelyn Column, built by Soane in 1785. The three panels along the bottom of this sheet, with a plan and two perspectives of Soane's 'east porch' design, suggest that this sheet may be a sketch for a presentation watercolour, like Gandy's famous composite view (No. 116).

79
Perspective View of the Mausoleum
Soane Office
May 1812?, watercolour, 91.5 × 66.5 cm

Inscr. 'Sir Francis Bourgeois/MDCCCXII' [on the sarcophagus]
SM 15/2/05

This large drawing is so much more richly decorated than the near-definitive design of 11 May 1812 (No. 77, SM 65/5/03) that it looks like an elaborate presentation piece. The lower storey of the mausoleum is here represented as stone and has pilasters with incised decoration. Under the central arch there are funereal urns in lunette openings as in an ancient Roman Colombarium, (illustrated frequently in Piranesi's *Antichità Romane* of 1756), with a free-standing *stele* below. The new design of Jacobean window is repeated here with sills like sarcophagi. The attic storey of the Gallery is hidden, underlining the mausoleum's status as an independent, monumental structure.

80

Perspective View of the Mausoleum

Soane Office

May 1812?, pencil, with grey, pink, blue, and yellow wash, 30.8 × 44.5 cm
SM Vol. 60/183

Soane included this drawing in a bound volume of designs and finished views of his works. Though the main structural elements here are as built, there are so many expensive decorative flourishes, like *stele* and Jacobean windows, that it is difficult to know whether this sheet belongs to the real or ideal history of the design. The chimneys on the skyline of the Gallery have been sketched in to the left.

81

Perspective View of the Mausoleum

R Chantrell

11 June 1812, watercolour, 68 × 114.5 cm
Inscr. 'June 11, 1812'
SM 15/2/06

Soane's pupil Chantrell drew this ambitious view while the mausoleum was already being constructed to a different design, recorded in the site view of 19 June 1812 (No. 95, SM 25/81/06). This sheet clearly belongs to the ideal rather than the real design process. Though very similar to the previous two views, there are changes in detail, such as the inclusion of the funereal motif of an eagle killing a snake on hemispheres over each altar.

82

Perspective View of the West Façade

JM Gandy

Probably second half of 1812, watercolour, 74 × 128 cm
Inscr. 'Sir Francis Bourgeois/MDCCCXII' [on the sarcophagus]
SM 15/2/03

This moody architectural fantasy is probably the 'Design for a mausoleum attached to the Gallery now building at Dulwich College' exhibited at the Royal Academy in 1813 (RA No. 836), though the date 1812 appears in Roman numerals on Bourgeois's sarcophagus. Gandy here uses the drama of an impending storm and an exaggerated scale suggested by the tiny figures at the foot of the mausoleum – both devices he could have learned from Piranesi's sublime reconstructions of ancient buildings.

The building shown here differs from the one executed in many ways (some of which have been explored in the last few sheets). We see here the distinctive design of the Jacobean windows (first encountered in No. 77) and the carved reliefs above the almshouse doors and in the attic. The mausoleum appears to be built of limestone with decorative elements of Portland stone; it has reliefs and seated figures surrounding the crowning cupola, which has a much steeper dome than finally built (see No. 74, 65/4/44). A more fundamental departure from the actual design is the idea of running the Gallery attic around the end block of the almshouses – and presumably all around the building. This would have lent the building unity and grandeur, but it would have made it impossible to light the old women's rooms on the first floor in any conventional fashion.

83

Perspective View of the West Façade

JM Gandy?

Probably 1812, watercolour, 72.5 × 129 cm

Inscr. 'Sir Francis Bourgeois/MDCCCXII' [on the sarcophagus]

SM 15/2/04

This view is a copy of the previous sheet, with the addition of another carved relief immediately under the arch of the mausoleum.

84

Plan of Half the Top Storey of the Gallery

Soane Office

May 1812?, pencil, with grey pink and blue wash, 55 × 68 cm

SM 65/5/01

In this upper storey plan, the arrangement of the Gallery skylights and the structure of the mausoleum cupola are clearly shown; both appear as built.

85

Plan and Section of the Framework for the Gallery Vaults

C Tyrell, G Basevi or *R Chantrell*

13 June 1812, pencil and watercolour, 25 × 45.5 cm

Inscr. 'Middle Room/June 13 1812'

SM Vol. 81/08

This measured drawing records the Gallery roof-timbers supporting the skylights. This drawing may have been made by Charles Tyrell (1795–1832), a pupil in Soane's Office from January 1811 to June 1816, who also executed two other detailed drawings at Dulwich (Nos. 88 and 89, SM Vol. 81/24 and 10).

86

Line Plan and Section of Half of the Gallery

Soane Office

May 1812?, pencil, with grey and yellow wash, 51 × 67 cm

SM 65/5/02

This drawing shows the chimney flues for the almshouses, built into the thickness of the west walls of the Gallery. An initial design for the chimneys is also recorded on this sheet.

87

Plan and Elevation of the Chimneys

Soane Office

May 1812? pencil, red ink, and grey wash, 26 × 41.1 cm

Inscr. on *recto* and *verso*: 'Three of these chimney tops wanted/Plan of the Chimney similar to those the other side'

SM Archive 6/25/23

This sheet is folded and was possibly used on site. It is worked on both sides. The *recto* shows a measured plan and elevation of the chimneys for the west side of the Gallery over the almshouses. This design provides for two chimney flues, and is related to No. 88 (SM Vol. 81/24). The *verso* shows the design of the chimney pots for the north and south ends of the gallery and has four flues. The designs differ in the amount of space left between each chimney flue, depending on their location. Both designs were executed as drawn here.

88

Elevation of West Façade Chimney

C Tyrell

1812, pencil and watercolour, 20 × 26.6 cm

Inscr. 'Drawing of Chimneys at Dulwich Gallery/C Tyrell'

SM Vol. 81/24

This scale drawing shows Soane's final design of the almshouse chimneys for the west façade, the chimneys over the north and south ends of the Gallery having wider spaces between the chimney stacks. This drawing relates to No. 87 (SM Archive 6/25/23).

89

Elevation of a Sarcophagus

C Tyrell

6 July 1812, black ink and watercolour, 19 × 25 cm

Inscr. 'CT/July 6th 1812'

SM Vol. 81/10

Drawn to scale, this elevation shows the final austere design of the sarcophagi decorating the exterior of the mausoleum. The sarcophagi were incised with fine lines to create a delicate play of light and shade across the plain Portland stone surface.

The Building in Progress: May to September 1812

90
The West Façade and Mausoleum Under Construction
G Basevi
29 May 1812, watercolour, 18.5 × 19.5 cm
Inscr. 'GB/May 29 1812'
SM Vol. 81/01

This watercolour view by George Basevi was copied into Soane's record book using a *trompe l'oeil* effect to make it look pasted on. The drawing shows the mausoleum at an early stage of construction and the foundations of the almshouses.

91
The Gallery Interior Under Construction
R Chantrell
29 May 1812, watercolour, 16.2 × 26.5 cm
Inscr. 'May 29 1812'
SM Vol. 81/02

Pasted into Soane's record book, this view shows the enfilade arches supported by timber centering. As in many progress views, much of the scaffolding is omitted to show the structure of the building more clearly. This drawing was made by Robert Chantrell (1792–1860) who worked in Soane's office from 1806 to 1836.

92
The Gallery Interior Under Construction
R Chantrell or *G Basevi*
3 June 1812, watercolour, 21 × 22 cm
Inscr. 'June 3 1812'
SM Vol. 81/04

This view of the enfilade, made one week after the previous drawing, shows the arches completed and the College visible beyond.

93
Construction View of the Mausoleum
G Basevi
3 June 1812, pen and grey wash, 34.5 × 24 cm
Inscr. 'GB/June 3 1812'
SM Vol. 81/03

This view of the erection of the Portland stone lantern omits the Gallery altogether to emphasise the mausoleum's apparently monumental proportions.

94
Bird's Eye View of the Gallery and Mausoleum
R Chantrell
13 June 1812, pencil and watercolour, 36.7 × 23 cm
Inscr. 'June 13, 1812'
SM Vol. 81/05

The light-filled character of this picturesque watercolour view of the half-built Picture Gallery recalls contemporary 'plein air' sketches of Roman ruins.

95
The West Façade Under Construction
R Chantrell
19 June 1812, watercolour, 23.5 × 34 cm
Inscr. 'Taken: Thursday June 18th and … View of the Mausoleum and part of the Picture Gallery at Dulwich College … R.C. Finished June 19th, 1812'
SM Vol. 81/06

Observed from under the shelter of a builders' shed, this view shows the installation of the timber framework for the almshouse roofs and the construction of the second storey of the north bay. The College chapel tower is visible in the distance.

96
The Mausoleum from Inside the South Almshouse
R Chantrell
19 June 1812, watercolour, 21.5 × 23. cm
Inscr. 'June 19th 1812'
SM Vol. 81/07

This view shows the mausoleum as seen from the ground floor room on the south west corner of the almshouse block.

97
The Enfilade and Mausoleum Under Construction
R Chantrell or *G Basevi*
29 June 1812, pencil and watercolour, 20 × 25.5 cm
Inscr. 'June 29 1812'
SM Vol. 81/09

Perspectivally complex, this view has two vanishing points, drawing the eye into the incomplete mausoleum and down the Gallery enfilade. The wooden framework for the vaults and skylights is dramatically silhouetted against the sky. An enlarged version of this view was made to illustrate Soane's twelfth Royal Academy lecture (see No. 113, SM 15/2/09).

98
The Enfilade Under Construction
G Basevi or *C Tyrell*
6 July 1812, pencil and watercolour, 23.5 × 26.5 cm
Inscr. '6 July 1812'
SM Vol. 81/11

This view down the Gallery's enfilade shows the roof-timbers as well as the foundations, with under-floor openings for the heating system.

99
The West Façade Under Construction
G Basevi or *C Tyrell*
6 July 1812, watercolour, 21.5 × 37.2 cm
Inscr. 'July 6, 1812'
SM Vol. 81/12

This and the two previous drawings were made on 6 July 1811 by either Chantrell or Basevi, who must have visited Dulwich together. An enlarged copy of this view was made by Soane's pupils to illustrate his twelfth Royal Academy lecture (No. 112, SM 15/2/10).

100
Interior View of the Almshouses and Mausoleum
C Tyrell
7 July 1812, watercolour, 23 × 34 cm
Inscr. 'July 7, 1812'
SM Vol. 81/13

A good idea of the dense layering of the scaffolding on the building site is given in this view. Through the arch to the left, lying on the ground, we can see the bowed wooden beams used to build the saucer dome of the mausoleum antechamber.

101
The Mausoleum from the Gallery Roof
R Chantrell
28 July 1812, watercolour, 22 × 16.7 cm
Inscr. 'RC/July 28 1812'
SM Vol. 81/14

The wooden framework for the mausoleum's saucer dome is in position, as is the structure for a pitched roof to protect the vault from the elements. The mausoleum lantern's glazing, provided by the firm Underwood and Co, is being installed.

102
The Enfilade Under Construction
C Tyrell
30 July 1812, watercolour, 22 × 21.5 cm
Inscr. 'CT/July 30, 1812'
SM Vol. 81/15

The ceiling vaults are in place and we see the installation of the skylights, which evidently had been redesigned since 5 March 1812 (compare No. 62, SM 65/4/58).

103
The Enfilade and Mausoleum Under Construction
Soane Office
1812, pencil and watercolour, 20 × 22 cm
SM Vol. 81/22

The vaults have been completed in this undated view, however the plastering has not yet begun. The horizontal timber spreaders below the vaults were designed to support the framework for the final plaster finish.

104
The Interior of the Mausoleum Under Construction
R Chantrell
29 July or 10 August 1812, pencil and

watercolour, 21.5 × 24 cm
Inscr. 'RC August 10 1812/Taken July 29th'
SM Vol. 81/16

In this view Robert Chantrell has already managed to evoke the dramatic lighting of this space which Soane was later to call 'lumière mystérieuse'.

105
One of Soane's Pupils Sketching
Soane Office
July 1812, pen and watercolour,
23.8 × 16.8 cm
Inscr. 'July 1812'
SM Vol. 81/23

Soane's pupils usually worked on progress views in pairs; some times they also sketched each other.

106
The West Façade
Soane Office
1812, watercolour, 20 × 32.5 cm
SM Vol. 81/17

This view shows the exterior of the west façade substantially complete.

107
The East Façade
GA Underwood or *G Basevi*
12 August 1812, watercolour, 19.5 × 31.2 cm
Inscr. 'August 12, 1812'
SM Vol. 81/18

The funds were never available to build the arcade Soane intended for the east façade. This view shows the point at which the building of this façade came to a halt. The structure to the right may be the 'old stable in front of the picture gallery' mentioned in the College minutes on 24 July 1814.

108
Plumbers' Lead Being Melted
G Basevi
13 August 1812, watercolour, 23.5 × 35 cm
Inscr. 'August 13, 1812'
SM Vol. 81/19

The lead parts of the building – gutters, flashing and roof covering – were cast on site. Records show that on 18 August the plumbing contractors removed 'old lead and cuttings' from the site for re-melting.

109
The West Façade from the South
R Chantrell
13 August 1812, pencil and brown ink, with grey and pink wash, 20.9 × 27.6 cm
Inscr. 'RC Aug 13th, 1812'
SM Vol. 81/20

Taken from the roof of the southern alms-houses, this fine view shows all the external structure of the building complete. The College chapel tower is visible to the right.

110
The West Façade from Gallery Road
R Chantrell
12 September 1812, watercolour,
22 × 37.7 cm
Inscr. 'Sep 2, 1812/RC'
SM Vol. 81/21

In early September the almshouse windows and doors had not yet been installed; perhaps at this stage, Soane was still uncertain about the almshouse window design.

Royal Academy Lecture Drawings: 1815

111
Royal Academy Lecture Drawing: The West Façade of the Gallery Under Construction
Soane Office
c. 1815, watercolour, 59.5 × 118 cm
Inscr. '20 Lect[ure] 12'
SM 15/2/08

This view, the twentieth illustration Soane used in his twelfth Royal Academy lecture, is either based on a lost progress view or is a conflation of those shown in the previous group. It shows the state of the building very soon after it was recorded by George Basevi on 29 May 1812 (No. 90, SM Vol. 81/01). Reduced versions of this drawing and the two following, made *c.* 1835, appear in Soane's manuscript copy of his lectures (SM Vol 160/20, 21 and 22).

112

Royal Academy Lecture Drawing: The West Façade of the Gallery Under Construction

Soane Office

c. 1815, pen and watercolour, 52.5 × 89.1 cm

SM 15/2/10

This view is an enlarged (and tidied up) copy of No. 98 (SM Vol. 81/12).

113

Royal Academy Lecture Drawing: View of the Gallery and Mausoleum Under Construction

Soane Office

c. 1815, watercolour, 58 × 54 cm

SM 15/2/09

A copy of No. 97 (SM Vol. 81/09).

114

The West Façade Under Construction

Soane Office

c. 1815, pencil and watercolour, 37.5 × 58.2 cm

SM 65/4/47

The scale of this sheet would seem to associate it with the Royal Academy lecture re-workings of the Dulwich progress views, rather than the views themselves. Though not copied from any surviving sheet, this view shows a similar moment in the building process to No. 95 dated 19 June 1812 (SM Vol. 81/06).

115

The West Façade Under Construction

Soane Office

c. 1815, watercolour, 58 × 122 cm

SM 15/2/11

This large view shows a similar stage in the building process as the previous, with the addition of amber-coloured glass and a Portland stone door for the mausoleum.

Gandy's Composite View of 1823

116

'Mausoleum and Picture Gallery with God's Gift College, Dulwich'

JM Gandy

1823, watercolour, 90 × 146 cm

Inscr. with the title: 'Dulwich College. The Picture/Gallery and the Mausoleum erected pursuant to the Will and at the expense of the late Sir Francis Bourgeois/This assemblage has been made to illustrate the doctrine of the Rev. T. F. Dibdin lately/promulgated respecting the advantages to the Public of liberal criticism and the unshackled freedom/of the Press'

SM P 265

Drawn by Gandy, this watercolour was exhibited at the Royal Academy in 1823 and, from 1835, in the North Drawing Room of Soane's house at Lincoln's Inn Fields. All eight parts here are so informative that it is worth treating them separately. This is especially true for the four real views, which in some cases offer the only record of the appearance of the building in the decade after it opened to the public.

Top left:
'Angular view from the Entrance Court agreeably to the original design'
The 'original design' in question shows a two storey entrance porch on the east side of the Gallery to balance the mausoleum on the west.

Centre left:
'The Picture Gallery'
This invaluable glimpse of the original interior shows Soane's skylights with solid crowns (later glazed); the original green oil cloth floor; and the disastrous steam heaters (within the green cylinders). The colour of the walls shown here is clearly not the 'burnt Oker' with which they were still covered at this date. This red is probably the colour Soane would have liked his galleries to be, and with which he finally had them painted (at his own expense) in 1829.

Bottom left:
'The plan of the building in its present unfinished and altered state'
This is probably the most reliable plan of the building as built, except that it shows the abandoned free-standing arcade on the east façade. 'Unfinished and altered' presumably

refers to the omission of the porch on the east side.

Top centre:
'View of the Entrance Front in its present unfinished state'
The title suggests that Soane regarded this façade as a mere patching up of the unfinished building recorded in the progress view of 12 August 1812 (No. 107, SM Vol. 81/18). This view omits the south door to the Gallery which was in use at this date. It also shows the small conical section of glazing at the centre of the otherwise solid crown of the skylights over rooms 1, 3 and 5 (which still appears in nos. 128, 148 and 9).

Centre:
'Central view from the Entrance Court agreeably to the original design'
This is a closer look at the 'double mausoleum' design illustrated top left.

Bottom centre:
'View of the Lawn Front of the building with the omission of the temporary entrance at the South-East corner'
This 'temporary entrance' is the south door into Room 1, still in use in 1939 and also omitted from the view of the east façade on this same sheet (for porches to this south door see Nos. 123 and 146). This west façade (or 'Lawn Front') view shows the simple round-topped sash windows Soane finally chose for the almshouses. Early twentieth-century photographs (see No. 157) show the area surrounding these windows within the brick arches to have been faced in ashlar, either when originally built or at some later date.

Centre right:
'The Mausoleum'
This view shows how much the mausoleum interior has been simplified since the designs of May 1811 (see Nos. 28 and 29, V&A 3307.109 and SM F91). This is the only surviving indication of its original colour.

Bottom right:
'The plan of the building agreeably to the original design'
This plan sets the Gallery, complete with east porch, within the wide version of the new quadrangle, last seen in Soane's plan of 7 August 1811 (No. 51, SM 65/4/31).

117
Ideal View of the East Façade of the Gallery
JM Gandy
c. 1823, watercolour on paper, 22 × 70.5 cm
DPG G44

This view is a duplicate of the central panel of the previous sheet showing the 'double mausoleum' design.

118
Ideal View of the Gallery from the South East
Soane Office
c. 1823, pen and ink with watercolour, 15.1 × 25.6 cm
V&A 3307.108

This small perspective view of the Gallery duplicates that seen in the top left corner of Gandy's composite view (No. 116).

119
Perspective View of the East Façade of the Gallery with an Arcade
CJ Richardson
c. 1828, pen and brown ink, 7.2 × 24.4 cm
V&A 3307.107

Charles James Richardson (1809–72), an articled pupil in Soane's office from February 1824 to January 1837, made this drawing and the two following as designs for lithographs illustrating Soane's *Designs for Public and Private Buildings* of 1828. Here the east façade of the Gallery is shown with the arcade but without the elaborate entrance porch seen in the three previous views.

120
Plan of the Gallery
CJ Richardson
c. 1828, pen and brown ink, 6.5 × 13.7 cm
V&A 3307. 107A

This plan is similar to that illustrated in the bottom left corner of Gandy's composite view (No. 116), but it omits the wall dividing the central chamber of the single storey almshouses. Like the previous sheet this plan includes the unbuilt arcade on the east façade of the Gallery.

121

Perspective View of the West Façade of the Gallery

CJ Richardson

c. 1828, pen and brown ink, 7.5 × 24.4 cm
V&A 3307.107B

This view is consistent with the one in Gandy's composite view (No. 116) except that more almshouse windows are here shown glazed.

George Tappen's Work at Dulwich College: 1805 to 1830

122

Plan and Elevation of the Stable Building

Charles Barry Junior

June 1858, pencil, black ink, grey, red and yellow wash. 53.4 × 74.2 cm
Inscr. 'Alleyn's College Dulwich/The Stable Building/Alterations & Adaptions/Scale 8 feet to an inch/Elevation towards yard/Elevation towards road/Plan of one pair floor/Section through stairs &c./Plan of ground floor/Charles Barry Junior/College Surveyor/June 1858.'
Dulwich College 177

This survey drawing made in 1858 by a later College architect, Charles Barry Junior, records the new stable block that George Tappen (College Surveyor 1805–30) was commissioned to build on 24 July 1814 (marked in red are Barry's proposed alterations).

123

The Gallery and 'New Porch' 1815–16

c. 1820, engraving, 5.5 × 12.5 cm
Dulwich College

This is the only surviving image of the 'New Porch' which was added to the south end of the Gallery. The architect (probably Tappen) was paid £13 3s and the bricklayer £99 8s 8d; many of the bricks were salvaged from the wall across the north end of the College quadrangle seen in No. 4. This modest porch served as the entrance to the Gallery until 1866. Also recorded in this view is part of the wall enclosing the 'Fore Court' to the west of the Gallery seen in plan in No. 135, presumably created following the decision in 1816 to provide external space for the alms women behind the Gallery.

124

Ground Plan of the West Wing of Dulwich College

George Tappen

1820, pencil, black ink and grey wash on paper, 65 × 80 cm
Inscr. 'Ground Plan/of the West Wing of Dulwich College/Shewing the intended improvements/1820./Drawing referred to by Particulars/& agreements dated Dec. 7, 1820/and signed by me/George Tappen'
Dulwich College

Tappen's proposal here (which was executed in full) can best be understood by comparison with Soane's survey drawing of 5 June 1811 (No. 9, SM 65/4/02). There is to be no major demolition, just a tidying up of the south-west corner so that the 'New Kitchen' makes a right angle corner for the site (even if the 'Pantry' runs off it at an oblique angle). In this process the internal 'Court' (see No. 9) disappears and the entire south range of the College is made coherent in plan. A passage is also created, between the south and west ranges, allowing access to the quadrangle from Gallery Road. Nos. 126 and 133 show what these plans look like in elevation.

125

First Floor Plan of the West Wing of Dulwich College

George Tappen

1820, pencil, black ink and grey wash on paper, 65 × 80 cm
Inscr. 'One Pair Plan/of the West Wing of Dulwich College/Showing the intended improvements/1820. Drawing referred to by Particulars/& agreements dated Dec. 7, 1820/

and signed by me/George Tappen'
Dulwich College

This sheet forms a pair with the previous drawing. Comparison with No. 9 shows that Tappen's work greatly increased the size of the Master's lodgings. Internal access to the west wing was now only possible from the first floor. Following the rehousing of the alms women in the Gallery block, the west wing was entirely given over to the school.

126

South Elevation of the South Range and East Elevation of the West Range of Dulwich College

George Tappen
1820, pencil, black ink and grey wash on paper, 67 × 81.5 cm
Inscr. 'Part of the South Elevation of the College/1820. Intended Improvements of the College/East Elevation on West Wing/End Elevation of West Wing/Drawing referred to by Particulars/& agreements dated Dec. 7, 1820/and signed by me/George Tappen'
Dulwich College

The three-bay, buttressed block to the left of the elevation at the top of this sheet shows the re-aligned south-west corner of the College. No. 133 shows what it looked like from the west (following the additions of 1831–46). Tappen's other structural alteration recorded in this elevation is the partial demolition of the south tower, which was necessary to make space for the four identical windows to the right of the Master's lodgings, as can be seen by comparing the plans of 1811 and 1858 (Nos. 9 and 135). Further to the right Tappen has sketched in pencil a new design for the tower and south façade of the chapel. No. 128 shows work carried out to this south façade of the chapel which is consistent with these faint pencil notes. We can assume therefore that Tappen was the designer.

The rest of the work shown here involves refacing existing elements (seen in Nos 3, 7 and 8) with picturesque Gothic details: the Master's lodging is given hoods over the windows, crenellations and finials; the west wing has had its Doric piers cut down into conventional buttresses and has bargeboards inserted beneath the gables.

127

View of Dulwich College from the North

J Rogers after *N Wittock*
1829, engraving, 12.6 × 17.5 cm
Inscr. 'Dulwich College/Published by/T Hinton of Warwick Square 1829/Drawn by N Wittock/Engraved by J Rogers'
Dulwich College

This print of the Old College quadrangle from the north should be compared with the same view taken thirty years earlier (No. 4 of 1796). The wall closing the quadrangle has gone and the west wing has obviously been refashioned by Tappen, thought not exactly as he proposed in the previous sheet. We also see here the otherwise undocumented transformation of the south range: the porch has grown into a crenellated tower; the famous Doric piers (which so influenced Soane) have been cut back to become conventional Gothic buttresses. It can be assumed that this work was also designed by Tappen and carried out at the same time as his other work on the College (between 1820 and 1829, the date of this print).

128

The Gallery and College Chapel from the South

c. 1840, brown ink, pencil and watercolour, 12 × 23.5 cm
Dulwich College

The 'mill pond' seen in No. 5 is still visible in the foreground of this crude watercolour drawing. To the right the chapel has been widened by the addition of a south aisle and a low structure added to the south side of its east end. The whole of the south façade now has a crenellated roof line as proposed (in pencil) on Tappen's 1820 elevation of this façade (No. 126). Barry's survey drawing of 1858 (No. 135) shows this arrangement in plan and No. 148 shows better the mini-tower Tappen created out of the remnants of the one seen in Nos. 2 and 3.

Sir Charles Barry's Work at Dulwich College: 1831 to 1858

129

Dulwich College from the North

From *Braley's Surrey*

1846, engraving, 26.5 × 34.5 cm

Dulwich College

The College here appears more 'picturesque' than at any other time in its history, largely because of the landscaping. The College has now lost the wall shown in the print of 1796 (No. 4); the gate has been moved further to the north to open up the quadrangle into an 'academic grove'. Sir Charles Barry's Neo-Gothic contributions – the new east range and western extension to Tappen's west range (just visible to the right) – add to the romantic atmosphere.

130

Dulwich College from the North

Rock & Co.

1849, engraving

Inscr. 'Rock & Co. London 1231/Dulwich College/Pub. Oct 10th 1849'

Location unknown

The opening of a short flight of stairs from the quadrangle down to the new garden is clearly seen in this view of 1849.

131

The Old Grammar School, Dulwich

Rock & Co

1849, engraving, 9 × 11.1 cm

Inscr. 'Rock & Co. London No. 1226/ Dulwich Schools/Sept 29th 1849'

Dulwich College

Designed by Sir Charles Barry in 1841, this old grammar school building survives to this day.

132

West Elevation of the East Wing and Section Through South Range of the College

Charles Barry Junior

1858, pencil and black ink, 53 × 74 cm

Inscr. 'No. 7 Dulwich College Elevation of East Wing and Section thro. Chapel as existing/Scale 8 feet to an inch/East Wing and Section thro. Chapel/Section thro' Butlers Pantry &c./Section thro' Library. Staircase & Chapel wall & Gallery/Section thro' Kitchen. Warden's Room &c'

Dulwich College

This survey elevation of the west (quadrangle) façade of the east wing shows the additions of 1831–46 made by Sir Charles Barry (College Architect from 1831 to 1858). A comparison with Taylor's print of 1796 (No. 4) and the relevant before-and-after plans (that is Nos. 9, 135 and 6) suggests that Barry Senior preserved the positions of doors, windows and Doric pilasters. His transformations occur at roof level: the pilasters are turned into buttresses and crowned with finials; the mansard windows are incorporated within the mini-gables of the main façade; and a new set of chimneys decorate the ridge of the roof.

This sheet is not just a record of past work: Charles Barry Junior sketches in pencil the design of two Gothic windows for the east end of the chapel and its south aisle. The Gothic windows which still survive at the east end of the chapel were presumably added therefore by Barry Junior.

133

Elevations of the remodelled West Wing of the College

Charles Barry Junior

1858, pencil and black ink, 53 × 74 cm

Inscr. 'No. 8 Dulwich College, Elevations/ Scale 8 feet to an Inch/Elevation of West Wing/End of West Wing/Elevation of Schoolmaster's Ho.' West Elevation of Building/Side Elevation of School'

Dulwich College

This complete set of survey elevations of the west wing of the College shows the work of both George Tappen and Sir Charles Barry. At the top left of this sheet, the east elevation is as George Tappen designed it (see No. 126). The right-hand end of the west elevation should be examined alongside the following drawing (No. 134) to provide a full picture of

Tappen's re-design of the Master's lodgings. This south-west corner of the College was so badly damaged by the 1944 bombing of Dulwich that it was completely re-built according to the 1948 designs of Austin Vernon architects. At the left end of the west elevation we see the three rooms (which still survive) added between 1831 and 1846 by Sir Charles Barry; to the left is a room (marked 'Solicitor's Office' on the 1864 survey plan, No. 136) with an ornamental gable above the oriel window; to the right the present Board Room (marked 'School' in 1864) is decorated with a fine Neo-Perpendicular window, with buttresses crowned by finials and with another figured gable. The room in between was the architect's office.

Charles Barry Junior at Dulwich College: 1858 to 1900

134
Elevation of the South Range
Charles Barry Junior
1858, black ink, 21.5 × 72.5 cm
Inscr. 'Dulwich College Elevation Scale 8 feet to an inch/South elevation'
This elevation shows the south range exactly as George Tappen built it. Barry Junior later modified the gabled block to the left, replacing the lower four windows with French windows (compare No. 162).

135
Ground Floor Plan to the College showing Alterations
Charles Barry Junior
c. 1858, pen and wash, 55 × 75.3 cm
Inscr. 'Alleyn's College, Dulwich./Plan/ Shewing Alterations and Adaptions /Charles Barry Junr/College Surveyor/7 June 185-' [Page torn]
Dulwich College

This plan records existing buildings with a few very minor alterations suggested in red. This and Barry's first floor plan which follows (No. 136) can be read together, and should be compared with Soane's survey of 1811 (No. 9). Together they give the best overview of fifty years of building.

The plan of the Gallery appears accurate, except that, at this date it cannot have had an aperture at the north as well as at the south end of the enfilade. This is the only indication of the original setting of the Gallery building, showing a walled 'Fore Court' to the west (partly visible in No. 123), with two constructions in the corners containing cubicles, lightly marked in pencil as 'closets to front in a line'. Those to the south were probably for the old women, and those to the north for the schoolboys.

The College buildings recorded here can be attributed as follows. The east range is a construction of 1728 (and probably earlier), refaced and slightly re-planned by Sir Charles Barry in 1831–46. The chapel dates from 1619, with an aisle added to the south and a refacing of the north, all probably by Tappen in 1820–30. The Master's lodgings in the south-west corner of the south range (later called the 'Chaplain's House') is an older building remodelled by Tappen, who also created the stables to its west along Gallery Road. The west range was remodelled by Tappen with three rooms added to its west façade by Sir Charles Barry. This plan also shows the more expansive landscaping of the College seen in Nos. 129 and 130.

The layout and names of the rooms in the east range suggest at this date that the old men still lived on the ground floor with accommodation for staff and boys above. The old women, however, have been moved from the west range to the Gallery almshouses, creating much more school space. This survey of the west range shows, on the ground floor, a 'boy's bath and washing room', a 'Reverends bed room', a dining room and kitchen, and, on the first floor (see No. 136), two large class rooms, a 'school' (in the present Board Room), and offices for the architect and solicitors.

136

Upper Floor Plan to the College

Charles Barry Junior

January 1864, pencil, pen and wash, 55 × 75.4 cm

Inscr. 'Alleyns College + Dulwich/As Now Existing/Jan[uar]y 1864/Plan of the One Pair Floor'

This survey plan can be read with the previous one of 1858, though it dates from January 1864. At this date, Charles Barry Junior had not made any significant alterations to the College Buildings which appear to remain as he found them in 1858.

137

Neo-Elizabethan Design Proposal for the North Tower of the Chapel

Charles Barry Junior

c. 1865, pencil on paper, 22 × 9.1 cm

Dulwich College 155

This fine detailed drawing shows an early proposal for the remodelling of the north tower of the chapel. This elegant Neo-Elizabethan design was rejected, however, in favour of a French Neo-Gothic design.

138

Elevation of the North Façade of the South Range of the College showing the Proposed New Cloister and Alterations to Chapel Tower

Charles Barry Junior

1865, pen and wash, 53.5 × 75 cm

Inscr. 'Alleyns College Dulwich/Extension of East Wing and New Cloister and alterations to Chapel Tower/and to Buildings generally/1st June 1865'

Dulwich College 179

This design, dated 1865, shows Charles Barry Junior's addition of a new French Neo-Gothic tower and cloister attached to the north façade of the south range, facing the College quadrangle. The present tower, built to this design though with many differences of detail, bears the date 1869. This drawing also shows Barry Junior's proposal to sink the quadrangle lawn, adding a short flight of steps up to the buildings at each end of the east and west wings, (compare No. 130 for the previous arrangement and No. 173 for the present arrangement).

139

Plan and Section of the First and Ground Floors of the East Wing showing Proposed Alterations

Charles Barry Junior

1 June 1865, pen with pink and grey wash, 53 × 57 cm

Inscr. 'Alleyn's College Dulwich Alterations and Extensions to East Wing and New Cloister/and Alteration of Chapel Tower/ Plan of East Wing/Scale 8 feet to an inch/ Plan of the One Pair Floor of East Wing shewing alterations & extension/Plan of the Ground Floor of East Wing shewing alterations/and extension/Charles Barry Archt./1 June 1865/Charity Commission/ Alleyn's College Dulwich/This is one of the Plans signed to in the Order/of the Board of 19th December 1865/Allen W Vale/Secretary' [indented with the Commission's seal]

This plan clearly shows Barry Junior's proposal for the interior refurbishment of the east wing. This work included removing the attic storey (seen in all the previous views of this wing: Nos. 4, 126 and 130) and lowering the roof as the section to the left of this drawing shows. This work was to increase the number of almshouse apartments to sixteen, to house not only the old men, who had always been here, but also the old women who were shortly to be removed from the Gallery block.

140

South Façade of the College

c. 1890, post card, 9 × 13.9 cm

Dulwich College

The single-storey building to the left of this view is shown in the 1858 survey plan (No. 135) as the 'Engine House'. We next see it all but annihilated by the 1944 bomb (No. 158).

141
Dulwich College From the North
Raphael Tuck & Sons
c. 1913, postcard, 9 × 14 cm
Inscr. 'Dulwich Old College'
Dulwich College

When Charles Barry Junior remodelled the east range of the College he removed almost all his father's work (compare Nos. 129, 130 and 132). By extending the whole range to the north he covered the oriel window on the north end. Though the fenestration remains the same, Barry Junior closed the attic windows facing the courtyard; he replaced his father's line of nine gables with four much smaller ones; and he removed the finials and cut back the buttresses in line with the rest of the quadrangle. Only the chimneys remain of Sir Charles's work. An inscription on the east side of this range records the year this remodelling work was completed as 1866. This photograph was taken after the war memorial, seen here in the foreground, was erected in 1913.

The Victorian Gallery

142
Interior View of the Gallery
Rock & Co
1849, engraving, 12.2 × 18 cm
Inscr. 'Rock & Co., London 1232/Picture Gallery Dulwich College/Pub Oct 10th 1849'
DPG Archive

Soon after this print was made the heating cylinders, seen here and in Gandy's interior view (No. 116, SM P 265), were removed. Since Gandy's time the floor cloth has been replaced by oak boards and a rail has been put up. Guido Reni's *Saint Sebastian* is already clearly visible at the north end of the enfilade, where it hung until the end of the nineteenth century.

143
Interior View of Galleries I–V
c. 1880, photograph, 15 × 20 cm
DPG Archive

This photograph was taken from Room I, the first room reached from Barry's entrance porch to the south. The visitor is appropriately greeted by the founders' portraits. The steam heaters have gone and a dado has been added, as recommended by Richard Redgrave, RA, in 1858.

144
Interior view of the Gallery
Joseph Dakin
1894, watercolour on paper, 60 × 45 cm
DPG Archive G 13

This charming watercolour reveals the hang of Room V at the end of the Soane enfilade. It also shows the arch opening into the present Room VI which was created out of the two-storey almshouse block in 1884. We also see here that the arches are picked out in a different colour and their thick, recently applied mouldings are gilded, as Barry Junior recommended to the Gallery Committee on 14 November 1876.

145
Interior of Gallery VI or IX
Emery Walker
c. 1900, post card, 9 × 14 cm
Inscr. 'The Dulwich Gallery (Interior No. 2)/Emery Walker ph. et imp.'
DPG Archive

This interior view shows one of the rooms created out of the almshouses in the 1880s.

146
The Gallery from the South-West
c. 1900, post card, 9 × 14 cm
Inscr. 'The Dulwich College Picture Gallery/ Printed at the Oxford University Press'
DPG Archive

Comparison with No. 123 shows that the walled courtyard for the almshouses has been removed and a carriage entrance put in its place. Barry's Neo-Renaissance south entrance porch, which appears in plan in No. 149, has replaced Tappen's more modest structure.

The two ornamental bases for a sundial and for plants, are in fact the altars of Soane's mausoleum (seen in No. 115, SM 15/2/11) 'recycled'.

147

The West Façade of the Gallery

c. 1900, post card, 9 × 14 cm

Inscr. *recto*: 'Dulwich Picture Gallery'; *verso*: 'The Mausoleum of Sir PF Bourgeois and Mr and Mrs Desenfans'

DPG Archive

The Victorian railings, the carriage gate on Gallery Road, and the landscaping are clearly in the same 'picturesque' taste as the College quadrangle seen in No. 129.

148

The Gallery and College Buildings from the South

c. 1900, post card, 8.7 × 13.9 cm

Dulwich College

The roof of Charles Barry Junior's French Neo-Gothic tower looms over the chapel. The Master and Warden of Dulwich College have moved to their new school down the road in *c.* 1870; the south-west corner of the old College is now called 'The Chaplain's House'. In the foreground a fence divides the chaplain's garden from the Gallery gardens.

To the left the large arch screening the end bay of the east façade of the Gallery is just visible; the whole Gallery is overgrown with ivy obscuring its architectural detailing.

Extending the Picture Gallery: 1908 to 1938

149

Plan and East Elevation of the Gallery: Existing and Proposed

E S Hall

1908, printed pamphlet, 43.8 × 34.5 cm

Dulwich College

These designs show the first phase of the building works carried out under Henry Yates Thompson, Chairman of the Gallery Committee from 1908. In the top plan and elevation the Gallery is shown as it was in 1908, with Charles Barry Junior's south porch of 1865 and his 1884 redesign of the almshouses. The lower plan shows the further conversion that Thompson envisaged – a 'gallery for small pictures' to run the entire length of the almshouses to the south and a larger curator's office and store within those to the north. Thompson also proposed a large new room at the centre of the east façade (the present Entrance Hall). The architect ES Hall's design for the exterior of this new room replicates the two screens at the ends of Soane's façade, with a large door in place of the arches. However, by adding a central emphasis Hall has destroyed the distinctive 'low-key' effect of Soane's east façade. These plans were accepted by the Picture Gallery Committee on 4 March 1909.

150

Gallery Interior; Room IX called 'The Gem Room'

c. 1910, post card, 9 × 14 cm

Inscr. 'Dulwich Gallery Interior of Small Room no. 9'

DPG Archive

This is the interior of the new room created under Thompson on the east façade (the present Entrance Hall) showing the huge door and damask wall-covering. Because so many highlights of the collection were hung here, this gallery became known as the 'Gem Room'.

151

Plan and East Elevation of the Gallery

E S Hall

1914, black ink with red and blue wash, 70 × 102 cm

Inscr. 'Dulwich College Picture Gallery/New Room 1914/East Elevation/Ground Floor Plan/Scale 8 ft = 1 in/E Stanley Hall MA ARIBA/Architect/54 Bedford Square WC'

Dulwich College

Henry Yates Thompson's original proposal had been to build only one new room, however the decision must have been taken soon afterwards to build five across the entire east façade. This plan and elevation of 1914 shows the rooms already finished (the present Rooms X, XI and the Entrance Hall) and one more in train (Room XII). The exterior elevation of Hall's Room X at the south-east corner replicates the design of Soane's screens which it covers up. His lower galleries, on each side of the Entrance Hall, (Rooms XI and XII) do not, however, replicate the five Soane arches which they cover (compare No. 149). Instead Hall created his own design of three arches separated by paired pilaster bands. The general feel is Soanean but the detail is misleading. The pilasters have no corresponding element in the Portland stone coping, as Soane's always do. Moreover these rooms look like the almshouse 'cottages' on the west façade (especially in 1952 when three windows were cut in each), thus losing Soane's contrast between his collegiate east façade and domestic west façade. The gap at the north end of this façade was not filled (by a fifth room) until 1936.

152

View of the North-East Screen

1920–35, photograph

SM Archive

This photograph shows the incomplete state of the east façade after the execution of the previous design. It is also the best record of the dramatic free-standing screens with which Soane articulated the two ends of his east façade.

153

Plan of the Gallery showing Proposed Alterations and Extension

JKH for *HS Goodhart-Rendel Architect*

5 November 1936, black ink with red and blue wash, 42 × 86.5 cm

Inscr. 'Dulwich College Picture Gallery/Proposed Additions and Alterations/Goodhart-Rendel/Architect/13 Crawford Street W1/Scale 8 Feet to 1 Inch/Drawing No. 10542/Drawn by JKH/Date 5.11.36'

DPG Archive

This and the two following drawings (Nos. 154 and 155), show Goodhart-Rendel's proposal of 1936 for completing ES Hall's series of new galleries across the east façade and for the enlargement of the existing entrance block at the south end of the Gallery. The entrance block was to encase Barry's existing structure and create space for the picture store, curator and committee rooms. The project was also designed to facilitate further expansion of gallery display space in the future.

154

Perspective Sketch of the West Façade with the Proposed Extension at the South End of the Gallery

JKH for *HS Goodhart-Rendel Architect*

5 November 1936, black ink, 42 × 61 cm

Inscr. 'Dulwich College Picture Gallery/Perspective Sketch Shewing Proposed Additions/Sketch Shewing Proposed/Future Extension/HS Goodhart-Rendel/Architect/13 Crawford Street W1/Drawing No 10543/Date 5.11.1936/Drawn By JKH'

DPG Archive

This perspective view shows Goodhart-Rendel's Soanean extension seen in relation to the Soane building.

155

Elevation of Proposed Extension at the South End of the Gallery

HCL for *Goodhart-Rendel Architect*

5 November 1936, pencil and watercolour, 46 × 59.5 cm

Inscr. 'Dulwich College Picture Gallery/Detailed Drawing of Proposed Additions/Scale Four Feet to Inch/Drawing No. 1054A/ HLC 5.11.36/Goodhart-Rendel/Architect/13 Crawford Street W1'

This beautiful watercolour clearly shows Goodhart-Rendel's top lit extension, encasing Barry's entrance porch with something larger and more Soanean. The project was not executed because of its £8,760 estimated cost.

156

East Façade of the Gallery

1938, photograph, 20 × 25.5 cm

Dulwich College

This rare photograph records the east façade as ES Hall envisaged it and Goodhart-Rendel completed it. It shows Hall's Rooms XI and XII (the lower galleries) with their three blind arches before windows were cut in them immediately after the Second World War. Hall's imposing central door was also hidden after the war with the addition of a porch in 1951 by Austin Vernon, the architect of the post-war rebuilding work.

157
West Façade of the Gallery
1938, photograph, 20 × 25.5 cm
Dulwich College

This 1938 photograph of the west façade shows the area around the almshouse windows within the surrounding arch to be faced in ashlar. It is not possible to assert from earlier views that this was the material originally used, but no records survive of any alterations to this area. Following war damage, the ashlar was replaced by brick.

War Damage: 1944

158
Bomb Damage: South-West Corner of the College and the Gallery
1944, photograph, 15 × 29 cm
Dulwich College

Before the bombing, this corner of the College looked as it did in 1858 (see Nos. 124, 126 and 133–6), except that the stable block along Gallery Road had already been demolished. Though the obliquely aligned 'Engine House' is all but obliterated, the rest of Tappen's 'Chaplain's House' can still be seen.

159
Bomb Damage: College and the Gallery West Façade
1944, photograph, 18.5 × 24.5 cm
DPG Archive

160
Bomb Damage: South Façade of the College
1944, photograph, 15 × 28 cm
Dulwich College

This photograph shows Tappen's alterations to the chapel and his 'Chaplain's House', with the French windows that Charles Barry Junior added to the gabled projecting section (compare No. 134).

161
Bomb Damage: Gallery West Façade
1944, photograph, 16 × 21 cm
DPG Archive

162
Bomb Damage: View through Gallery VI
1944, photograph, 17.5 × 15 cm
DPG Archive

Charles Barry Junior's vault in Room VI (visible here) was replaced in 1952 with one of modern design. This photograph enabled Rick Mather, the architect of the Gallery's 1999–2000 refurbishment, to recreate the Barry original.

163
Bomb Damage: Gallery Interior Rooms I–V
1944, photograph, 21.3 × 16.8 cm
DPG Archive

This is the first view showing the Edwardian glazing of the sloping lights. While the framework of the Gallery skylights survived the blast, the glazing was shattered and much of the vault's plaster work was loosened.

The Old College and the Gallery Rebuilt: 1945 to 1998

164
Plan of the Gallery Showing Post-War Rebuilding and Proposed Alterations
Austin Vernon
1948, coloured ink, 51 × 76.5 cm
DPG Archive

In this early plan for reconstructing the Gallery, Vernon shows Barry's entrance block transformed from porch to service facilities, only accessible from inside the Gallery. The entrance is now into the north almshouse block (the present Room VII).

This idea was abandoned following Sir John Summerson's advice that Barry's entrance porch should be demolished, thus 'restoring the clear cut lines of the original building' (see No. 167). Summerson also proposed that the 'ground in front of the mausoleum should be laid out simply as a lawn, coming right up to or very near to the building.' Both these suggestions were acted upon and consequently the entrance to the Gallery was moved to the centre of the east façade. Barry's entrance had contained vital service facilities and in 1951, it was resolved that these should be installed in Goodhart-Rendel's north-east corner gallery.

165
Plan, Elevation and Section of the Porch on the East Façade
Austin Vernon
February 1951, coloured ink, 51 × 77 cm
Inscr. 'Dulwich Picture Gallery/Section/ Elevation/Elevation/Roof/Plan/Foundation/Arthur Davis Consultant/ Four Feet to One Inch/Austin Vernon FRIBA/ 21 Catherine Place/Westminster SW1'
DPG Archive

It had now been decided that the main entrance to the Gallery should be in the centre of the east façade into ES Hall's 'Gem Room'. These designs show the narrow porch Vernon added for this new entrance to protect the pictures from the outside air. This elevation also shows Vernon's new windows piercing Hall's blind arches on the east façade (compare No. 156).

166
Plan and Elevation of the College Road Entrance Gates to the Gallery
Russell Vernon
1951, pencil on tracing paper, 56 × 65 cm
Inscr. 'College road entrance gates to Dulwich Picture Gallery/Russell Vernon MAE ARIBA/21 Catherine Place SW1/Scale 1/2" = 10"'
DPG Archive

These gates were designed by Austin Vernon's nephew Russell. In the 1999–2000 refurbishment the gates were retained though hung from new posts.

167
South Façade of the Gallery
Martin Charles
1981, photograph
DPG Archive

All but a single wall (glimpsed on the right) of Barry's porch has been removed, though its 'shadow' is still visible in the brickwork.

168
East Façade of the Gallery
Martin Charles
1981, photograph
DPG Archive

This photograph records the appearance of the east façade from 1953 to 1999, with Austin Vernon's porch and with the six windows cut into ES Hall's originally blind arches (compare No. 156).

169
South and West Elevations of the Old College
Austin Vernon
c. 1948, pen with pink, blue, grey, and brown washes, 71 × 68 cm
Inscr. 'Alleyn's College of Dulwich suggested restoration after war damage/Austin Vernon FRIBA/Architect/21 Catherine Place/ Westminster SW1/The South Elevation/ The West Elevation/8 Feet to 1 Inch/The old College existing/Office extension/ New Entrance to Chapel and Cloisters/ New Cottage/Entrance to Gallery Garden/ Picture Gallery'
DPG Archive

This design for the rebuilding of the College following war damage should be compared to Nos. 133 and 134. Vernon has 'amputated' the damaged south-west corner, replacing the oblique 'Engine House' with a new, correctly-aligned, Georgian style cottage. The south elevation of the College (above) shows Tappen's façade with its three left hand bays removed, but otherwise untouched (compare No. 134). The west elevation (below) shows everything remodelled to the right of Sir Charles Barry's School Room (the present Board Room, see No. 133). As Vernon's inscription notes, the new arched entrance runs directly into Charles Barry Junior's cloister, unlike the previous access from Gallery Road which was further to the left. The following drawing shows how this looks in plan (compare No. 135).

170

Ground Plan of Half the South Range and the West Wing of the College

Austin Vernon

c. 1948, pen with pink, blue grey and brown washes, 71 × 68 cm

Inscr. 'Alleyn's College of Dulwich suggested restoration after war damage/Ground Floor Plan/8 Feet to 1 Inch/Austin Vernon FRIBA/Architect/21 Catherine Place/Westminster SW1'

DPG Archive

This and the two following designs should be read together and compared with the survey plan of 1858 (No. 135). Areas marked in grey are to be left unaltered; areas marked in yellow are to be restored to their pre-damaged form, and those in blue represent proposed new building. As in the previous design, Vernon here cuts the damaged corner out of the building – that is everything to the south or west of the room marked 'Master's Wine Cellar' in the 1820 plan (No. 124). The only part to be replaced is the plant room (marked 'heating' on the plan) and the cottage. This proposal differs from that executed only in the area marked 'Meeting Room', 'Vestry' and 'Choir Vestry', which here is shown as restored building and which in the event was completely rebuilt.

171

First Floor Plan of Half the South Range and the West Wing of the College

Austin Vernon

c. 1948, pen with pink, blue grey and brown washes, 71 × 68 cm

Inscr. 'Alleyn's College of Dulwich suggested restoration after war damage/First Floor Plan/8 Feet to 1 Inch/Austin Vernon FRIBA/Architect/21 Catherine Place/Westminster SW1'

DPG Archive

This plan is consistent with the previous one.

172

Plan and Elevation of the West Façade of the College

Austin Vernon

September 1953, black ink with red, green and brown washes, 58 × 73 cm

Inscr. 'The Old College Dulwich Village/Proposed Garages/September, 1953/Scale 1" = 8'0"

DPG Archive

This elevation is consistent with the two previous plans and shows this west façade of the College as built.

173

Dulwich College from the North

John Hammond

April 2000, photograph

DPG Archive

Charles Barry Junior's remodelling of the east wing survived until the first half of this century when, in about 1950, three projections for stair-towers were added as part of the conversion of the whole of the east range into flats for the elderly (compare with No. 156).

174

The Gallery and South Façade of the South Range of the Old College and Chapel

Martin Charles

1981, photograph

DPG Archive

In all the designs reproduced above (see especially the elevation No. 169), Vernon intended to retain most of Tappen's Chaplain's House (six bays in all). In the event he decided to demolish and remodel them, creating three storeys instead of two out of the same height, cutting a 'patio' area between the gabled block and the chapel, and eliminating from the whole of the south façade any surviving traces of Victorian charm.

175
Galleries I–V
c. 1960, photograph, 25.5 × 20.5 cm
DPG Archive

In the meeting of December 1952, it was agreed that fabric would be the ideal covering for the Gallery walls. However, due to lack of funds it was decided that the pictures would be 'hung on the bare but smooth and even plaster walls'. The Gallery walls were in fact given a coat of grey distemper and the edges of the arches were re-gilded.

176
Galleries I–V
Martin Charles
1981, photograph
DPG Archive

In 1980–1 funds were provided by the Friends of Dulwich Picture Gallery to redecorate the galleries. The then Director, Giles Waterfield, restored them to a colour close to Soane's original red and rehung them with the paintings double-stacked to recreate the appearance of the Gallery in the nineteenth century.

177
The Mausoleum
Martin Charles
1981, photograph
DPG Archive

178
The Interior of the Mausoleum
Martin Charles
1981, photograph
DPG Archive

179
The Interior of the Mausoleum showing Soane's *'lumière mystérieuse'*
Martin Charles
1981, photograph
DPG Archive

180
Interior Room IX
Martin Charles
1981, photograph
DPG Archive

Converted from almshouses to gallery space by Charles Barry Junior in 1865, this exhibition space has been replicated in Room VI by Rick Mather Architects.

181
Interior Room XII
Martin Charles
1981, photograph
DPG Archive

This photograph records ES Hall's vault design, used for Rooms XI and XII. These vaults were redesigned by Rick Mather Architects in order to show Soane's attic storey panels on the east façade.

Rick Mather Architects: Refurbishment and New Building: December 1995 to May 2000

182
First Floor Survey Plan
Rick Mather Architects
1996, black ink

This survey plan records the arrangement of the Gallery skylights prior to refurbishment. Those in the central enfilade are Soane's; that in the south-west corner room (Room IX) is Barry Junior's; those in Room VII, and along the east front are ES Hall's (in the case of Room XIII executed by Goodhart-Rendel); the two remaining (Rooms VI and VII) are Vernon's.

183a
East Façade – Existing
Rick Mather Architects
16 October 1996, black ink on tracing paper, 59.5 × 84 cm
Inscr. 'East Façade – Existing'
Rick Mather Architects

183b
East Façade Proposed Options One and Two
Rick Mather Architects
16 October 1996, black ink on tracing paper, 59.5 × 84 cm
Inscr. 'East Façade Proposed Option One/ East Façade Proposed Option Two'

Rick Mather Architects

'Option One' is the executed design. This design is best understood by comparison with Nos. 149, 156 and 168. As well as blocking up the windows in Rooms XI and XII (for security purposes), Mather has replaced Hall's three arches facing the exterior of these rooms with replicas of the arches with which Soane articulated his east façade, thus facing each room with five arches. Lowering the vaults in these two rooms means that these five arches can now be seen lining up with the five corresponding panels in the attic story, which survive from Soane's original façade. At the same time Mather squares off Vernon's porch (by filling its corners, compare No. 165) to create a central bay of the same form and dimensions as the two Soanean end bays.

184

Existing and Proposed College Road Elevation

Tim Carter for *Rick Mather Architects*
10 January 1997, black ink on tracing paper, 59.5 × 84 cm
Inscr. 'Tender/Existing College Road Elevation/Proposed College Road Elevation/Proposed Courtyard Elevation/Dulwich Picture Gallery/Provision of Additional Gallery Space and/Ancillary Visitor Facilities'
Rick Mather Architects: Drawing No. 385/1016

185

Existing and Proposed Chapel Elevation

Tim Carter for *Rick Mather Architects*
10 January 1997, black ink on tracing paper, 59.5 × 84 cm
Inscr. 'Tender/Existing Chapel Elevation/Proposed Chapel Elevation/Dulwich Picture Gallery/Provision of Additional Gallery Space and/Ancillary Visitor Facilities'
Rick Mather Architects: Drawing No. 385/1015

186

Proposed Ground Plan

Rick Mather Architects
1996, coloured, 32 × 45 cm
Inscr. 'New Build/Existing Building/Wall to be Removed/opening up the garden/Mausoleum/Soane building/Gallery services/Art education centre/cloister/Lecture room/cafe'
DPG Archive

187

Gallery Interior Rooms I–V

John Hammond
May 2000, photograph
DPG Archive

This view shows Soane's famous enfilade refurbished prior to the rehang of the collection. An oak board floor has been laid, the Victorian gilding of the arches has been removed, and new climate and light control systems have been installed. Soane's mutules under the main cornice have been made visible by the removal of the 1970s strip lighting.

Bibliography

Allen, LB., 'The Last testament of Sir Francis Bourgeois' (Manuscript, Sir John Soane's Museum: Private Correspondance IX/D/2/2) published in Waterfield, G. (ed), *Soane and Death. The Tombs and Monuments of Sir John Soane*, (exhib. cat. Dulwich Picture Gallery, London, 1996).

AMS John Architects and Robert George Architects, *Old Dulwich College and Picture Gallery. Conservation Plan.* (Document, Dulwich Picture Gallery Archive, 1998).

Balantine, A., 'First principles and ancient errors: Soane at Dulwich' in *Architectural History 37* (1994).

Beresford, R., *Dulwich Picture Gallery. Complete Illustrated Catalogue*, (London, 1998)

Birnstingl, H.J., *Sir John Soane*, (London, 1925).

Bolton, A.T., *The Works of Sir John Soane: 1753–1837*, (London, 1924).

Bolton, A.T. (ed.), *Lectures on Architecture by Sir John Soane...As delivered to the Students of the Royal Academy from 1809 to 1836 in Two Courses of Six Lectures each*, (London, 1929).

Dejardin, I. and Shawe-Taylor, D., *Rembrandt to Gainsborough. Masterpieces from Dulwich Picture Gallery*, (exhib. cat. Museum of Fine Arts, Houston/Speed Museum, Louisville, 1999).

Dibdin, Rev. T. F., 'A Day at Dulwich College' in *The Museum* (London, 1822–24).

Du Prey, P. de la Ruffinière, *Sir John Soane. Catalogues of Architectural Drawing in the Victoria and Albert Museum*, (London, 1985).

Graves, A., *The Royal Academy of Arts. A Complete Dictionary of Contributors and their Work from its Foundation in 1796 to 1904*. (London, 1904).

Green, B., *Dulwich Village*, (London, 1981).

Lacey, V., *Sir John Soane's Dulwich Picture Gallery* (Document, Dulwich Picture Gallery Archive, December 1996).

Piggott, J. R., *Charles Barry Junior and the Dulwich College Estate*, (London, 1986)

Piggott, J. R., *Dulwich College. A Brief History and Guide to the Buildings*, (London, 1990).

Private Stings Book 1805–29, (Manuscript, Dulwich College Archive).

Richardson, M., 'Soane's Use of Drawings' in *Apollo* (April 1990).

Richardson, M., 'John Soane: The Business of Architecture' in *Georgian Architectural Practice, Georgian Group Symposium*, (London, 1991).

Richardson, M., 'Learning in the Soane Office', in *The Education of the Architect. Procedings of the 22nd Anual Symposium of the Society of Architectural Historians of Great Britain*, (London, 1993).

Richardson, M. and Stevens, M.A. (eds.), *John Soane Architect. Master of Space and Light.* (exhib. cat. Royal Academy, London, 1999).

Soane, Sir J., *Soane Notebooks III*, (Manuscript, Sir John Soane's Museum).

Soane, Sir J., *Soane Day Books 1811–12*, (Manuscripts, Sir John Soane's Museum).

Soane Museum, *Building in Progress: Soane's Views of Construction*, (exhib. cat. Sir John Soane's Museum, London, 1995).

Stroud, D., *Sir John Soane Architect*, (London 1984, revised 1996).

Tilman Mellinghoff, G., 'Soane's Dulwich Picture Gallery Revisited', in *John Soane Academy Editions Monographs*, (London, 1983).

Waterfield, G.(ed.), *Collection for a King. Old Master Paintings from the Dulwich Picture Gallery*, (exhib. cat. National Gallery of Art Washington/ Los Angeles County Museum of Art, 1985).

Waterfield, G., *Soane and After. The Architecture of Dulwich Picture Gallery*, (exhib. cat. Dulwich Picture Gallery, London, 1987).

Waterfield, G.(ed.), *Soane and Death. The Tombs and Monuments of Sir John Soane*, (exhib. cat. Dulwich Picture Gallery, London, 1996).

Watkin, D. *Sir John Soane. Enlightenment Thought and the Royal Academy Lectures*, (Cambridge, 1996).

Young, W., *History of Dulwich College*, (London, 1889).

Published by Dulwich Picture Gallery,
Gallery Road, London SE21 7AD

Designed by Herman Lelie
Typset by Stefania Bonelli
Production co-ordinated by Uwe Kraus GmbH
Printed in Italy by Musumeci

ISBN 1 898519 16 1

British Library Cataloguing-in-Publication Data:
A catalogue record is available from the British Library